ANGLESEY

Flowering Plants and their Habitats

GARETH ROWLANDS

Published by Gareth Rowlands

ISBN 978-1-5272-2578-7

July 2018

In memory of John Cave MBE
(*1934-2018*)

Design and layout by: jenksdesign@yahoo.co.uk
Printed by Cambrian Printers, Aberystwyth, Wales

"If you look the right way, you can see that the whole world is a garden."
Frances Hodgson Burnett (The Secret Garden, 1911)

A list of the flora of the island entitled 'Flowering Plants and Ferns of Anglesey' by R.H. Roberts was published in 1982. His work identifying and keeping notes of the plants he encountered over 25 years of research, together with records from a number of other observers, form the basis of the list. However, the book, informative as it is, contains no illustrations. He also comments that the Welsh common names of plants have been omitted "because there is, at present, no generally accepted list".

Over time the size and distribution of plant populations change. Anglesey has a wealth of rare plants but also species of plants that are in decline. Inevitably changes to the environment have taken place through an increase in tourism, changes in agriculture and the introduction of industry. Efforts have been made by various organisations to save Anglesey's wildlife and to restore species that have been lost over the years. Much of this is carried out through the protection and management of habitats essential for those particular species.

Natural Resources Wales (NRW) protects 60 Sites of Special Scientific Interest (SSSIs) of which four are managed as National Nature Reserves (NNRs), such as Newborough Warren. Anglesey County Council helps protect wildlife through its planning policies and through the management of areas such as the Dingle Local Nature Reserve (LNR) in Llangefni and the Holyhead Breakwater Country Park. The North Wales Wildlife Trust has five nature reserves including the National Nature Reserve (NNR) at Cors Goch. The National Trust own many properties nationally where wildlife conservation is a primary objective. On Anglesey the Trust has the care of extensive sections of the coastline around Cemlyn Bay. The RSPB manages nature reserves at South Stack and Valley Wetlands. The organisation is also restoring wetlands on its Malltraeth Marsh and Cors Crugull reserves. All of these sites are of European and global importance.

This book is not intended to serve as a comprehensive local flora list, to do so would require a much larger volume. The purpose is rather to provide an introduction to the flowering plants of the island of Anglesey which will be useful to the residents who wish to know more of the richness of their surroundings and to visitors who wish to learn a little of the beauty and wildlife of the area they visit. To discover the world of plants it is necessary to appreciate the principles of taxonomy or classification and understand the parts of a flower, plant reproduction, pollination, fertilisation, growth, the interaction with animals and also the habitat or area which they inhabit. These disciplines are introduced to aid the beginner or keen enthusiast to appreciate the complexity and diversity of plants.

Habitats vary considerably, particularly in soil types and water availability and over time living organisms often need to change in order to survive. In other words they become adapted to their habitats. This means that species have evolved special features that help them to survive. Anglesey has a number of natural habitats including coastal heath, fens, mudflats and salt marshes, ponds, lakes and rivers as well as some of the most extensive sand dunes in Wales. These habitats are considered together with a description of the flowering plants likely to be most frequently encountered there. Grasses, sedges and rushes have been mentioned only briefly as they are very difficult to identify. The plant description follows the following format:-

English common name - Latin name - Welsh common name - Family - Photograph.

There follows a brief outline of the identification features of the plant, its type of growth, height and flowering period and where applicable conservation status according to the International Union for Conservation of Nature (IUCN) Red List of Threatened Species. Where appropriate in pale green boxes is given a description of the possible origin of the common name or names of the plant and, purely for interest, its culinary use and any medicinal properties.

The Isle of Anglesey Area of Outstanding Natural Beauty (AONB) is administered by the County Council's Countryside and AONB Service. The following is a brief adapted overview of the work carried out and is reproduced by kind permission of Anglesey County Council. (Website details on p.127)

"The Isle of Anglesey AONB has one of the most distinctive, attractive and varied landscapes in the British Isles. Anglesey was designated as an AONB in 1966 in order to protect the aesthetic appeal and variety of the island's coastal landscape and habitats from inappropriate development.

The AONB is predominantly a coastal designation, covering most of Anglesey's 201 kilometre coastline but also encompasses Holyhead Mountain and Mynydd Bodafon along with substantial areas of land which form the essential backdrop to the coast. The total coverage of the AONB on Anglesey is approximately 221 sq Kms (21,500 hectares). The landscape of the AONB reflects the varied underlying geology and is a diverse mixture of marine and terrestrial habitats, including rugged cliffs, heath land, sand dunes, salt marshes and mudflats.

The AONB contains many habitats which have statutory protection because of their nature conservation value. These designations include: Special Areas of Conservation (SACs); Special Protection Areas (SPAs); National Nature Reserve (NNR); Sites of Special Scientific Interest (SSSIs); Local Nature Reserves (LNRs). These support a wealth of habitats and wildlife.

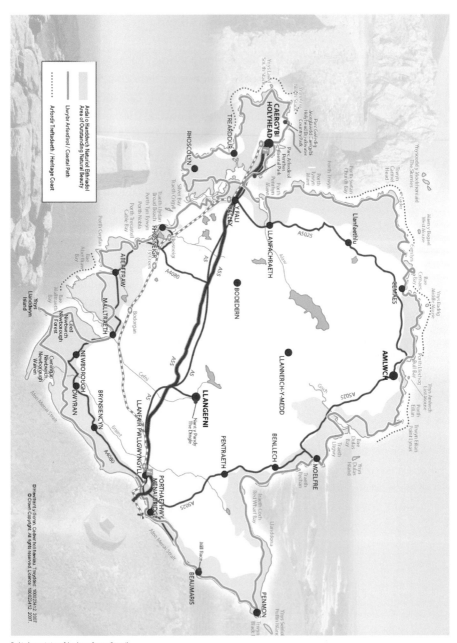

6

CONTENTS

Introduction   8

Types of habitat   9

The Protection of Wild Flowers   10

Linking geology and biodiversity   11

Adaptations of plants to water availability   13

Succession   15

Classification   16

Flowering plant reproduction, growth and leaf structure   22

Coastal Habitats

    ● Cliffs   29

    ● Sand dunes   41

    ● Shingle   72

    ● Mudflats and salt marshes   80

Wetlands

    ● Fens and marshes   87

    ● Ponds, lakes and rivers   106

Calcicoles and Calcifuges   113

Index of Flowering plant photographs   123

Acknowledgements   127

INTRODUCTION

Anglesey is an island with over 100 miles of coastline and possesses a variety of habitats, such as sea cliffs, dunes and beaches, salt marshes and mudflats. These habitats provide homes for a wide variety of animals and also harbour a varied flora. Inland much of the island is low lying agricultural land. Numerous areas are flooded and marshy, providing a different set of conditions for living organisms. Anglesey also has a wide range of often complex rock formations, ranging from Precambrian to Carboniferous. Added to this are some excellent examples of the effects of Quaternary glaciations. In summary, the rocks vary not only in age but also in origin and chemical composition.

The soils that are formed range from lime-rich to acidic, mineral deficient soils. However, the pattern of distribution is modified or obscured in many places by the overlying glacial deposits and by the deposition of blown sand, alluvium and peat which have accumulated over time. Thus the complexity of the soil and the effect of maritime influences, together with a mild, equitable climate and adequate rainfall, provides all the conditions necessary to support a rich and interesting flora.

The development of tourism and the creation of the Coastal Path around the island has had significant implications for nature conservation on Anglesey. It has been necessary to put in place measures to protect vulnerable habitats such as sea cliffs with seabird colonies and the prevention of the erosion of sand dunes. Consequently, almost the entire coastline has been designated an Area of Outstanding Natural Beauty (AONB).

On Anglesey four main kinds of maritime habitat may be recognised. These are cliffs, sand dunes, shingle beach, mud flats and salt marshes.

Non-maritime habitats include wetlands, such as fens and marshes, and ponds, lakes and rivers.

Two groups of plants which need specific soil pH requirements are calcicoles and calcifuges.

These types of habitat will be considered in turn, together with a brief description of the identification features of selected flowering plants together with the common name, genus and species name, Welsh common name, and the flowering plant family to which it belongs. As an aid to identification, included with the image is a description of the type of growth cycle of each plant - Annual, Biennial, Perennial; Height; Period of flowering; Abundance status - if Endangered, Vulnerable or Rare.

Where appropriate reference is made to the origin of the Latin or common name and any culinary or medicinal use. Although herbs may appear harmless because they are used in cooking, with some species concentrated doses can be lethal. References to culinary or medicinal uses of selected species of plants are for interest only and should not be considered as a recommendation for their use. Many medicinal applications can be beneficial but a medical expert should always be consulted before making any changes or additions to prescribed medications. Herbs should be used in moderation. Herbs, like medications, are potent and must be taken wisely and with caution because they may interact with other medications. Herbs rarely cure diseases but they may help to relieve symptoms.

THE PROTECTION OF WILD FLOWERS

Anglesey has a rich and varied coastline most of which is an Area of Outstanding Natural Beauty (AONB) attracting many local residents and tourists to its shores each year. The coastline is also home to an abundance of diverse wildlife. Not only are rare animals found on the island but also a wealth of interesting plants, such as the county flower, the dainty Spotted Rock Rose which flowers early in the morning. The South Stack Fleawort is endemic to South Stack and cannot be found growing anywhere else in the world! Many wild flowers are in serious decline or endangered, and they need to be protected. Plants in decline on the island include Chamomile, Pale Dog Violet and Lesser-Butterfly Orchid. Anglesey has also lost plants such as the Dwarf Juniper, the Starved Woodsedge, Pennyroyal, Red Helleborine and others. It is not illegal to pick wild flowers, as long as you have the right to be on the land. However, this right depends on a variety of confusing legislation. When studying wild flowers it is essential to establish that you are not dealing with a protected species or a protected site. A common sense approach is required. If a species is obviously abundant, there is no harm in picking a flower for closer examination but it should never be uprooted! However, the more scarce a plant is in any one place, or is known to be uncommon or even rare, it should be left untouched.

With today's widespread use of digital photography and mobile phone cameras, taking photographs is an excellent way of recording wild flowers. However, careless behaviour can sometimes cause more damage than picking flowers as popular sites may become heavily trampled underfoot where photographers have lain their equipment on the ground. As a general rule picking wild plants should be avoided. It is hoped that the many colour photographs in this book and their location on the island will help enthusiasts identify at least some of the plants! Always treading carefully of course.

LINKING GEOLOGY AND BIODIVERSITY

For a relatively small area of land Anglesey is unusual in that it possesses a great variety of rock formations. Since this is a key factor in determining the distribution of habitats and species it helps to account for the great range of flora found on the island. Rock formations on Anglesey range from the earliest layers of sedimentary rocks in the Pre-Cambrian period to the most recently deposited clays, sand and gravels left by the glaciers of the last Ice Age. The rocks vary not only in age but also in origin and chemical composition. Consequently, the great diversity of soil types found on Anglesey may be related directly or indirectly to the underlying rocks and to the effects of glaciation since the pH of newly formed soils is determined by minerals in the soil's parent material.

The island is subject to maritime influences, has a mild climate and adequate rainfall. In addition there are inland areas with still and free-flowing waters further increasing the diversity of conditions for the growth of plants. A number of diverse habitats have developed ranging from the lime-rich soils that occur around Penmon, Red Wharf Bay and Lligwy Bay to the acid, mineral deficient soils of Holyhead Mountain. Soil pH is a measure of the acidity or alkalinity of a soil. The optimal pH range for most plants is between 5.5 and 6.5. However, many plants have adapted to thrive at pH values outside this range. Thus plants have evolved to grow in different habitats that often reflect the pH of the soil.

The acidity or alkalinity of a soil is important to plants as soil pH plays a major role in nutrient availability. Plants that thrive on lime-rich soils are called calcicoles. Those that cannot tolerate alkaline (basic) soils are called calcifuges. These plants grow only or mainly on acidic soil. Calcicoles and calcifuges are described on page 113-122.

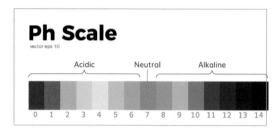

Plants require specific amounts of minerals such as nitrogen, phosphorous and potassium for growth. Generally, minerals are taken up by the roots from the soil solution and if a soil is too acid or too alkali plants cannot take up these minerals and growth is affected. Where soils have a pH that falls outside the optimal pH range some plant species have evolved and can thrive successfully whereas other species cannot tolerate any extremes of pH. Below a pH of 5.5 some nutrients such as nitrogen, phosphorus, and potassium are less available. Heathers grow in these acid soils. Above a pH of 7.5 iron, manganese, and phosphorus are less available. Wild Thyme grows well in these alkaline soils.

Apart from topography and soil type the ability of a plant to live in a particular environment is determined by a number of factors which include rainfall, water availability, light, temperature, relative humidity, wind and salinity. This book considers some of these factors in specific locations on the island. For example, the wind-swept cliff tops of South Stack provide harsh conditions and the thin, acidic soil means that water supplies are minimal. The plants growing on the sand dunes of Newborough are subjected to salt spray from the sea carried on strong onshore winds and rapid drainage of rain water occurs through the sand. The Cefni salt marsh is frequently submerged by the tides providing conditions which can only be tolerated by specialised plants called halophytes.

ADAPTATIONS OF FLOWERING PLANTS TO DIFFERING WATER AVAILABILITY

Plants face a dilemma. In order to produce glucose by the process of photosynthesis (see page 27) plants must take in carbon dioxide through the stomata or pores in their leaves, combine it with water in the chloroplasts using sunlight energy and release the waste product, oxygen, into the atmosphere. At the same time plants must not lose too much water by evaporation through these open pores by the process called transpiration. If a plant loses more water through its leaves than it takes up from the soil through its roots then the plant wilts and the leaves droop reducing the surface area for photosynthesis. To counteract this the stomata, found on the underside of the leaves, close during periods when water loss is greater than water uptake.

Plants can be classified into three groups in relation to the prevailing water supply:

- **Mesophytes** - plants living in habitats where there is adequate water supply.
- **Xerophytes** - plants living in conditions where water is not readily available.
- **Hydrophytes** - plants found growing in water.

Most land plants growing in temperate regions are called mesophytes. They are adapted to grow best in well-drained soils and moderately dry air. The water they lose through the pores in their leaves is readily replaced by uptake of water from the soil through their roots, so they do not require any special means of conserving water.

Xerophytes are plants living in conditions with low water availability and have developed modified structures to prevent excessive water loss. They may live in hot, dry desert regions or cold regions where the soil water is frozen for much of the year, or in exposed, windy locations. Marram Grass (*Ammophila arenaria*) (see p.43-45) is a xerophyte. It grows in sand dunes where there is no soil, rainwater drains away rapidly, and is exposed to winds, salt spray and a lack of shade from the sun. Plants growing on the cliffs of South Stack and the surrounding mountainside also tolerate harsh conditions: dry, well-drained acidic soils, exposure to direct sunlight and high winds. Many of the plants growing here have evolved adaptations to reduce water loss. For example, Bell Heather (*Erica cinerea*) (see p.32) has reduced leaf size with the leaf margins in-rolled.

Hydrophytes grow submerged or partially submerged in water. Unlike xerophytes they have no need to reduce water loss and have certain advantages to being surrounded by water. However, in order to survive in an aquatic habitat they have different problems to overcome. For example, water contains twenty times less oxygen than air. To compensate for this the stems and leaves of many hydrophytes have large air spaces forming a reservoir of oxygen and carbon dioxide. They allow diffusion of oxygen from the aerial portions of the plant into the roots. Thus the roots do not have to depend on obtaining oxygen from the soil. These gases also provide buoyancy to the plant. (For more detail on hydrophytes see p.107.)

SUCCESSION

The distribution of species does not necessarily remain the same over long periods of time. Ecosystems are dynamic and subject to change. Organisms and their environment interact. A change in the environment affects the organisms and a change in the organisms affect the environment. The change in community structure and species over time is called succession. In any area, over time, new organisms replace existing ones, that is species diversity increases until a stable state is established. This is known as a climax community, for example, a mature woodland.

There are two types of succession, primary and secondary.

● Primary succession

Primary succession is the sequence of changes following the introduction of species into an area that has not previously supported a community, for example, bare rock. The sequence of stages, with the different species and structures, is called a sere. Each seral stage alters the environment and makes it more suitable for other species to inhabit. The invading species may outcompete those that are there already and in this way succession progresses.

There are three main types of primary succession:

Xerosere:
When the plant succession develops in a xeric or dry habitat, it is called xerarch or xerosere. For example, sand dune succession (see p.42).
Hydrosere:
The plant succession which starts in the aquatic environment is called hydrarch. A series of changes taking place in the vegetation of hydrarch is called a hydrosere. For example, a fen or marsh.
Halosere:
A special type of sere which begins on a salty soil or in saline water, for example, salt marsh (see p.81-82).

Secondary succession

Secondary succession occurs after an event that deeply disturbs an existing, stable ecosystem when most above-ground vegetation and living organisms disappear from the region, such as that caused by a fire. Though it appears that the region is uninhabited, in fact the soil remains fertile and contains enough organic matter to support the reappearance of life, because it contains seeds, bulbs, and underground rhizomes etc. A secondary succession has the same overall sequence as primary succession but the succession is far more rapid.

Human interference can affect a succession and may prevent the development of the climax community by: e.g.

- Grazing by sheep and cattle maintains grassland and prevents the shrubs and trees of a normal succession from growing.
- Farming of land removes all except deliberately introduced species and great effort is made to exclude all others.
- Deforestation removes a community of large trees and replanting of small trees may take place.
- Trampling of dunes by the public.

CLASSIFICATION

The plant kingdom contains organisms which possess the pigment chlorophyll in order to carry out the process of photosynthesis. They are classified into a number of different groups or phyla. The main phyla include Bryophytes (Mosses and Liverworts) and Pteridophytes (Ferns) which all reproduce by spores whereas Gymnosperms (Conifers) and Angiosperms (Flowering plants) reproduce by seeds. **This book deals only with flowering plants.** When describing living organisms taxonomists look for differences and similarities between them and place similar organisms closely together and dissimilar ones further apart. There are seven major levels (taxa) in a hierarchical biological classification system.

Kingdom-phylum-class-order-family-genus-species

Identifying flowering plants is not an easy task. Books are available to aid identification but some botanical knowledge and a familiarity with botanical terms is required. Successful identification comes with experience and the ability to observe carefully, making a note of distinguishing features, then matching these to the text and illustrations in a book. It does help to recognise the main features of the major plant families, such as the rose family, the pea family, the cabbage family etc. Many books use keys as an aid to identification but a knowledge of technical terms is required in their use. Using this book it is hoped that the colour photographs together with a brief description of the plants expected to be found in a particular habitat will help the enthusiast in their identification.

Some biological terms:

subspecies = a subdivision of a species (abbreviation subsp. or spp.)
native = a plant that grows in an area without human introduction either deliberately or accidentally.
endemic = native and restricted to a certain place.
habitat = place where an organism or a biological population normally lives or occurs.
taxa (pl. of taxon) = any unit used in biological classification, or taxonomy. Taxa are arranged in a hierarchy from kingdom to species.
phyla (sing. phylum) = a taxonomic rank at the level below kingdom and above class in classification.
taxonomy = the branch of biology concerned with naming and classifying the diverse forms of life.
hierarchy = a classification system based on ranking groups in ascending order from large groups to small groups.
key = device used by biologists for identifying unknown organisms. They are constructed so that the user is presented with a series of choices about the characteristics of the unknown organisms; by making the correct choice at each step of the key the user is ultimately led to the identity of a specimen.

genus = taxonomic category ranking used in classification that is below a family and above a species level, and includes group(s) of species that are structurally similar.

species = a group of similar organisms that can breed together to produce fertile offspring.

The following describes the classification of one particular species of the many orchids found on Anglesey. The hierarchical classification of the Bee Orchid.

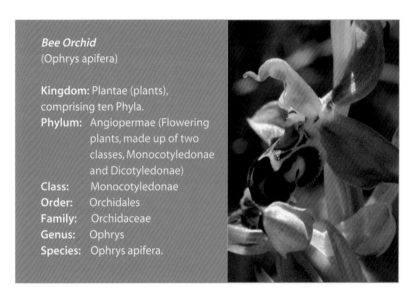

Bee Orchid
(Ophrys apifera)

Kingdom: Plantae (plants), comprising ten Phyla.

Phylum: Angiopermae (Flowering plants, made up of two classes, Monocotyledonae and Dicotyledonae)

Class: Monocotyledonae

Order: Orchidales

Family: Orchidaceae

Genus: Ophrys

Species: Ophrys apifera.

In this book, for the purposes of classification, only the terms **family, genus** and **species** are used.

Binomial system

Many plants have common names which may differ from one country to another or even within different areas within the same country. This can be confusing and to overcome the problem plants are named according to the binomial system.

This system was devised by the Swedish scientist Carl Linnaeus in 1753 and is based on using Latin as an international language. The name is always written in italics and is made up of two parts, genus and species. The genus is the first name and begins with a capital letter. The species name follows and does not have a capital letter. *Geranium pratense* is the scientific name for the flower commonly known in the UK as Meadow Cranesbill. *Geranium* is the name of the genus, *pratense* is the specific name given to this member of the *Geranium* genus. All other members of the same genus have names beginning *Geranium* and ending with unique specific names. For example *Geranium lucidum* is the scientific name for Shining Cranesbill. The first time the scientific name is used in a text, it is written in full but if used again in the same text the genus name may be abbreviated e.g. *G.pratense*. This system means that the plant is given precise identification worldwide whereas the common name is not. Also each plant has its own unique scientific name but enables scientists to recognise that two species are closely related, e.g. *G.pratense and G.lucidum*.

Meadow Cranesbill (*Geranium pratense*)   Shining Cranesbill (*Geranium lucidum*)

Genera and families

Three similar genera *Erodium, Geranium* and *Pelargonium* have the same characteristics in regard to their seed pods which resemble the long beaks of certain birds. That characteristic is the basis for the names: *Geranium* evokes the crane (Greek *geranos*), *Pelargonium* the stork (*pelargos*), and *Erodium* the heron (*erodios*). Because their seed pods resemble cranes' and storks' bills they are given the common names Cranesbill and Storksbill and are placed in the family Geraniaceae.

Although one common feature enables similar plants to be grouped together in a family, other features have to be considered to classify the plants further into their taxonomic ranks of genus and species.

Cranesbills belong to the genus *Geranium* whereas Storksbills belong to the genus *Erodium*. One main difference is the arrangement of the leaves. In the genus *Geranium* the leaves are palmately-lobed i.e. have the lobes spreading radially from a point, like fingers on a hand. In the genus *Erodium* the leaves are pinnately-lobed i.e. the leaves have lobes arranged on either side of a central axis like a feather. An additional feature enabling the plants to be grouped into a third genus is the number of stamens or anthers: *Erodium* flowers have five fertile stamens, *Geranium* flowers have ten fertile stamens and *Pelargonium* flowers have fewer than ten fertile stamens, commonly seven or five.

Common Storksbill (*Erodium cicutarium*)

Herb-Robert (*Geranium robertianum*)

Common names

Common names for plants are generally used by the local population. Their usage may be restricted to a small area having a unique dialect, a county, a region or a country. Common names do not always correctly describe or classify a plant. (For example, Sawgrass is not a member of the Grass family, Poaceae, it is a member of the Celastaceae family.) Similarly a bulrush is not a rush but a sedge. A true rush is the Common Rush of the genus *Juncus*. The main advantage of using common plant names is ease of usage and common understanding in certain geographical areas. However, there may be several common names for a single species of plant and this would be very confusing to scientists in different countries. International agreement has enabled each plant species to be given a unique name to avoid such confusion. The science of naming plants is governed by a series of internationally accepted rules and regulations contained in the International Code of Botanical Nomenclature, first formulated in 1905.

Examples of Confusing or Misleading Use of Common Plant Names

In North America corn (*Zea mays*) is also called maize. But in England corn is a general name for grain or, more specifically, wheat, whereas in Scotland corn refers to oats.

White Waterlily (*Nymphaea alba*) is also known as White Water Rose, White Nenuphar, Bobbins, Cambie Leaf, Can Dock, Common Water Lily, European White Lily, Flutterdock and Platter Dock. If the German, French and Dutch names are included it has even more common names!

Bell Heather (*Erica cinerea*), found commonly on Anglesey, has several common names including Bell Ling, Black Heath, Carlin Heather (Carlin, from Old Norse *kerling*, meaning hag or witch), Cat Heather, Crow Ling and She-heather.

Traveller's tree (*Ravenala madagascariensis*) is also called Traveller's palm. But it is neither a tree nor a palm, it only resembles a palm plant. It actually belongs to the banana family, *Musaceae*.

The differences between Angiosperms and Gymnosperms

Flowering plants or Angiosperms have seeds that are enclosed within an ovary, while Gymnosperms have no flowers and have unenclosed or 'naked' seeds on the surface of scales. Gymnosperm seeds are often configured as cones. An important characteristic that differentiates Angiosperms from Gymnosperms is the endosperm or food store found in the seeds of flowering plants. This provides the advantage of nourishment for the newly developing plant before the leaves are able to photosynthesise.

Flower of Cherry showing male and female organs

Conifer cone

FLOWERING PLANT REPRODUCTION

In order to identify flowering plants some knowledge of plant structure is required. It is beyond the scope of this book to include a glossary of terms to include leaf structure, root and stem morphology etc. However, the following section describes flower structure, pollination, fertilisation and seed germination as a basic requirement to identification.

Flower structure

The flower is the reproductive part of the Angiosperm plant. Many species have flowers that are hermaphrodite, that is, the flowers contain both male and female parts. Flowers of different species exhibit a great variety in their appearance but similar patterns can be seen. A flower consists of four modified leaves arranged from the outside to the centre. The following describes the structure of a typical insect-pollinated flower.

- The outermost ring of structures are the sepals which are usually green and protect the flower in bud.
- Inside the sepals is the ring of petals. These are brightly coloured to attract insects, usually have a scent and produce nectar, again to attract insects.
- Inside the petals are the male parts of the plant, the stamens. Each stamen consists of a long, slender stalk or filament at the end of which are the pollen sacs or anthers in which pollen grains are produced. When mature the pollen sacs split to release the pollen.

⚙ In the centre of the flower are the female parts collectively called the carpel or pistil. The lower part is called the ovary which contains the eggs or ovules. Projecting from the ovary is the stalk-like style. This ends in the flat, receptive surface, the stigma.

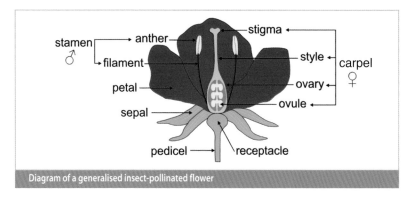

Diagram of a generalised insect-pollinated flower

Pollination

Successful pollination results in the transfer of pollen from the pollen sac or anther to the stigma of a plant of the same species. This is essential in order that the pollen grains containing the male gametes are brought into contact with the female part of the flower so that fertilisation can be achieved. Pollinators such as bees are attracted by large, coloured petals, by scent and nectar. An insect may visit several different species of flowers but only a compatible pollen grain will grow a pollen tube down the style and complete fertilisation in the ovule. The style contains enzymes that destroy pollen tubes originating from the pollen of flowers of a different species.

Wind pollinated flowers, such as grasses and many trees, lack such showy flowers. Instead, they produce larger quantities of light, dry pollen from small, plain flowers that can be carried from plant to plant on the wind.

Honeybee pollinating a flower

Hoary Plantain
(*Plantago media*)

Grass flower
(*Bromus sp.*)

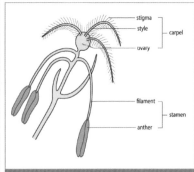

Diagram of generalised wind-pollinated flower

Marsh Foxtail
(*Alopecurus geniculatus*)

Fertilisation

When a pollen grain lands on the stigma, the stigma produces a sugary solution in which the pollen grain germinates producing a pollen tube. The threadlike pollen tube grows down through the style and pierces one of the ovules in the ovary allowing the male and female gametes to fuse forming a zygote. Each zygote now has the full set of paired chromosomes.

gamete = sex cells containing only a single set of chromosomes. The pollen grain contains the male chromosomes and the ovule contains the female chromosomes.

chromosome = occurs in the cell nucleus and consists of a single molecule of DNA which carries the genes determining heredity. Chromosomes are strand-like and occur in pairs in the nucleus. There are different numbers of chromosomes in different species of all living organisms. During gamete formation each gamete receives half a strand. During fertilisation the resulting zygote contains one strand from the male and one strand from the female thus ensuring variation in the species.

zygote = the cell formed by the union of a male sex cell (a sperm) and a female sex cell (an egg or ovule). The zygote develops into the embryo following the instruction encoded in its genetic material, the DNA.

fertilisation = the joining of a sperm and an ovum to form a zygote.

germination = the process by which a dormant seed begins to sprout and grow into a seedling given the right conditions.

photosynthesis = the chemical reaction that uses energy from sunlight to convert water and carbon dioxide into glucose with the release of oxygen. Photosynthesis takes place in special structures in the cells called chloroplasts. Leaf cells which carry out photosynthesis are packed with chloroplasts.

respiration = a chemical process which requires oxygen and takes place in the mitochondria of cells. Energy stored in glucose is released together with the waste products carbon dioxide and water.

diffusion = the movement of molecules down a concentration gradient, from high to low.

Seed and fruit development

Following fertilisation, the development of the seed and fruit takes place. Each fertilised ovule or zygote divides many times to form the embryo plant, located within the seed. Each seed now contains a nucleus which contains half the chromosomes from the pollen grain and the other half from the ovule.

Examples of fruit containing seeds

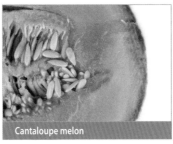

bean

Cantaloupe melon

Peach

The ovary develops into the fruit, which may contain one or several seeds, according to the species. This may be eaten by animals helping to disperse the seeds to a new location to avoid competition with the parent plant. Given the right conditions the seed will develop into a new plant. This process is called germination. Seeds need to be transferred away from the parent plant. If they grow too close to the parent it will cast shade over the developing seedling thus preventing it from carrying out the process of photosynthesis successfully. By avoiding competition with the established parent plant the seedling will be more successful at obtaining water and minerals from the soil.

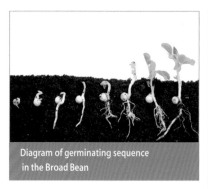

Diagram of germinating sequence in the Broad Bean

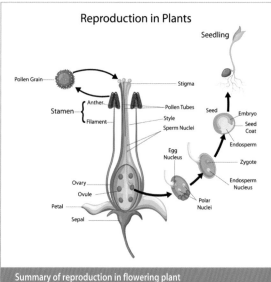

Summary of reproduction in flowering plant

Plant growth

Most animals stop growing after reaching a certain size. In contrast most plants continue to grow throughout their lives. However, this indeterminate growth does not last forever as plants, of course, die eventually.

There are three forms of plant life cycles.
- Annuals - these plants complete their life cycle, from seed germination through flowering and seed production to death, in a single year or less.
- Biennials - flowering plants that take two years to complete their lifecycle. In the first year the seed germinates, grows leaves, stems and roots, then it enters a period of dormancy over the colder months.

In the second year it will continue to grow, flower, produce seeds and die.

⬤ Perennials - plants that grow for more than two years and may live for many years. These include trees, shrubs and grasses as well as many herbaceous plants. However, horticulturists usually categorise perennial plants into two types: woody plants and herbaceous perennials. Woody plants are trees and shrubs whose above-ground parts persist over the winter and resume growth in the spring. **This book focuses mainly on herbaceous plants.** These are non-woody and die back each autumn leaving the underground parts to survive the winter allowing the plants to re-sprout in the spring. Most of the plants described are in this category.

Leaf structure

In the same way that animals need to respire constantly, so do plants! During the day plants carry out both processes of respiration and photosynthesis but at night only respiration takes place as the process of photosynthesis requires light.

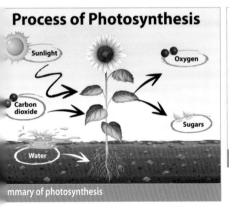

Summary of photosynthesis

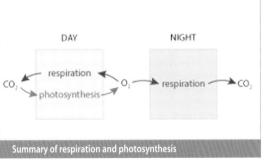

Summary of respiration and photosynthesis

Most of the carbon dioxide plants need for photosynthesis diffuses into the leaves from the atmosphere. The waste product of oxygen diffuses out. These gases pass in and out of leaves through small pores, called stomata, usually found on the underside of leaves.

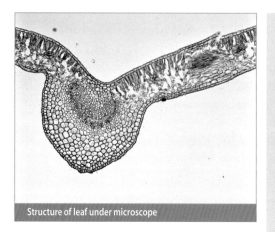

Structure of leaf under microscope

Leaves:
- have a large surface area to capture maximum light.
- are thin to allow light to penetrate to lower layers of cells.
- have upper cells packed with chloroplasts .
- have air spaces to allow gases to diffuse.

LEAF ANATOMY

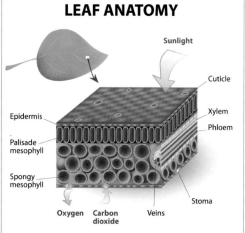

Internal structure of a leaf

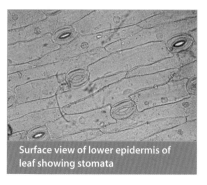

Surface view of lower epidermis of leaf showing stomata

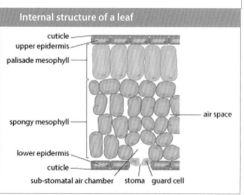

COASTAL
HABITATS

Cliffs

CLIFFS

At South Stack steep steps descend to the iron suspension bridge which spans the gap between the mainland and the small island of Ynys Lawd and the lighthouse. In early summer Holyhead mountain and the cliffs around South Stack are a wonderful sight, ablaze with the colour of wild flowers. Bell Heather in full bloom turns the mountainside a beautiful shade of mauve. In some parts the combination of Heather with the vibrant yellow flowers of Gorse creates a colourful patchwork on the coastal cliffs.

Coastal heath at South Stack

Plants growing here have to survive the harsh conditions of mountainside or cliff. High winds and thin soil mean that the transpiration rate is high and water supplies are minimal. Many of the plants show xeromorphic adaptations in order to survive. The vegetation is dominated by a few species of which Heather, the Heaths (*Erica cinerea* and *E.tetralix*), Western Gorse and Purple Moor Grass (*Molinia caerulea*) are most common. During the summer months a beautiful display of maritime wild flowers also colour the area.

Common Heather or Ling (*Calluna vulgaris*) Grug Family Ericaceae

A low-growing evergreen with sprays of tiny, purplish-pink flowers. Height to 60cm. Flowers mid Jul-Sep. It is usually at its best in late August.

The genus name *Calluna* is derived from the Greek verb *kalluno* which means 'to sweep'. Traditionally, a type of brush was made by tying bunches of heather to a handle to make a coarse broom for sweeping floors; they were standard household items in the days of 'dirt floors' and are still associated as 'witches' brooms'. Other past uses of Heather include the dyeing of wood and the tanning of leather, bedding material for livestock and humans, for thatching roofs, as a fuel, in rope-making, and to repair holes in tracks and roads. It is still used as an ingredient in toiletries.

Bell Heather (*Erica cinerea*) Clychau'r Grug Family Ericaceae

Heather thrives in low-nutrient acidic soils making the cliffs and mountain slopes where thin peaty soil lies upon granite ideal for the plant to flourish. Bell Heather is distinctive with its dark purple-pink, bell-shaped flowers forming clusters around the stem, and short, dark green needle-like leaves in whorls of three. Height up to 60cm. Flowers Jun-Oct.

The flowers are larger and brighter than *C.vulgaris* and appear slightly earlier in the summer.

Bell Heather is an important nectar source for all kinds of insects including Honeybees, Buff-tailed and Red-tailed Bumblebees, Ruby Tiger Moths and rare Silver-studded Blue Butterflies. The honey produced from bees feeding on Heather is dark and fragrant.

The following description of the leaf structure of *Erica cinerea* shows how the xerophytic features of the leaf enable the plant to survive the harsh conditions on the wind-swept cliff tops.

- There is a thick waxy cuticle on the leaf surface. This helps to minimise water loss by evaporation from the leaf, making it virtually waterproof.
- The leaf is 'in-rolled' i.e. instead of being flat it is coiled over on itself. This reduces leaf surface area and reduces water loss by transpiration.
- The stomata are sunken and located in depressions below the leaf surface. This helps to reduce air movement and produces a microclimate of still, humid air thus reducing transpiration.
- The number of stomata is less than in the equivalent area of a mesophyte thus reducing the spaces for water to be lost.

Cross-leaved Heath (*Erica tetralix*)
Grug Deilgroes Family Ericaceae

A bushy evergreen plant with leaves in a whorl (radiating in a circular or spiral arrangement from a point) of four, arranged up the woody stems. The plant has numerous heads of eight to ten rose pink, urn-shaped flowers. Height to 70cm. Flowers Jun-Sep.

The following describes and illustrates a selection of other flowering plants growing in abundance at South Stack. Two species of Gorse may be found:

A very spiny, evergreen shrub with densely packed yellow, coconut scented flowers, in bloom for much of the year. Height to 3m. Flowers Jan-Dec.

Gorse was at one time used as an under-thatch on Welsh cottages beneath the final layer of straw. It was also used as a fuel, notably in bakers' ovens. The ashes made an excellent soil dressing. Another use for the alkali-rich ashes was as a detergent in washing.

Gorse *(Ulex europaeus)* **Eithinen Ffrengig Family Fabaceae**

Similar to *U.europaeus* but smaller and more delicate. Flowers only in late summer. Height 30-100cm. Flowers mid Jul-Oct.

Western Gorse *(Ulex gallii)* **Eithinen Man Family Fabaceae**

Also known as Sea Pink. The narrow leaves form a basal clump from which pink flower heads are borne on long, thin, leafless stalks. Perennial. Height 5-30cm. Flowers late Apr-Jul.

Thrift *(Armeria maritima)* **Clustog Fair Family Plumbaginaceae**

Thrift was featured on the reverse of the old three-penny coin minted up until 1970. Thrift is rarely used in herbal medicine, though the dried flowering plant is reputed to have antibiotic properties and has been used in the treatment of obesity, some nervous disorders and urinary infections.

Spring Sqill (*Scilla verna*) Seren y Gwanwyn
Family Asparagaceae

Like the Bluebell, this and the many other Squills used to be included in the Lily family, Liliaceae. Following DNA analysis they have been reclassified as members of the Asparagus family (Asparagaceae).

Sometimes mistaken for a stunted Bluebell it bears spikes of up to 12 pale bluish-lilac flowers. With their short, strong stems they are ideally adapted to exposed windswept grassy cliffs. Perennial, growing from a bulb. Height 5-15 cm. Flowers Apr-early Jun.

Kidney Vetch (*Anthyllis vulneraria*) Plucen Felen Family Fabaceae

Large, kidney-shaped flower heads, which may be yellow, orange or occasionally red. Perennial. Height to 60cm. Flowers May-Sep.

The species name 'vulneraria' (vulnus = wound) means wound healer. Externally applied, the plant was an ancient remedy for skin eruptions, minor wounds, cuts and bruises. Internally, it was used as a treatment for constipation and as a spring tonic. Kidney Vetch was also once used as a remedy for kidney disorders and is also sometimes used in cough-relieving teas. The plant provides food for a number of beetle and moth larvae but, most importantly, is the sole food plant for the caterpillars of the rare small blue butterfly, *Cupido minimus*.

Rock Sea-spurrey has cylindrical fleshy leaves with small, lilac-pink flowers which are very sticky and hairy. Salt tolerant. Perennial. Height 5-15 cm. Flowers Jun-Aug.

Rock Sea-spurrey (*Spergularia rupicola*)
Tywodwlydd Y Mor Greigiau
Family Caryophyllaceae

Sea Campion has fleshy, waxy, grey-green leaves with abundant white flowers on short straight stems. Flowers are joined at their base to form a tube and surrounded by sepals forming a bladder-like structure. Perennial. Height 8-30cm. Flowers Apr-Aug.

Sea Campion (*Silene uniflora*) Gludlys Argor
Family Caryophyllaceae

Plants of the genus *Silene* have roots that contain the compound saponin which, although a mildly toxic substance, has long been used as soap for washing clothes, hair etc. Marbled coronet Moths (*Hadena confusa*) lay their eggs in the seedpods.

A low sprawling plant with yellow to orange or red tinged flowers in clusters at tips of the stalk. Perennial. Height 10-50cm. Flowers May to Sep.

Common Bird's-foot-trefoil (*Lotus corniculatus*)
Pys y Ceirw Family Fabaceae

This plant has around seventy common names! These include Bacon and Eggs, Fingers and Thumbs, Birds' Claws, Cats' Claws, Old Woman's Tooth, Grandmother's Slippers, Shoes and Stockings, Butter Jags, Butter and Eggs, Pattens and Clogs and Tom Thumb. The genus name *Lotus* refers to the shape of flower, while *corniculatus* means 'horned'. Bird's-foot-trefoil was incorporated into the protective wreaths of golden flowers worn on Midsummer Night (known as Herb Evening). It's trifoliate leaves link to the Trinity, while the horn-like seed pods allude to the devil. Trefoil is believed to be the incarnation of Tom Thumb (a tiny man) as the leaves resemble the Devil's fingers.

All parts of the plant are poisonous, containing cyanogenic glycosides (hydrogen cyanide). In small quantities, hydrogen cyanide has been shown to stimulate respiration and improve digestion, but in excess can be lethal.

A delicate plant with numerous small pale lilac flowers. Winter annual to biennial. Height 5-25 cm. Flowers Feb-Jun.

Danish Scurvygrass (*Cochlearia danica*)
Llwylys Denmarc Family Brassicaceae

A salt tolerant species. In recent times it has been seen on roadside verges which have been treated with salt to prevent icing in winter creating an ideal habitat.

Sprawling to semi-erect stems with small blue to deep-blue flowers gathered into tight clusters. Biennial. Height 5-30 cm. Flowers May-Aug.

Sheep's-bit Scabious (*Jasione montana*)
Clefryn Family Campanulaceae

English Stonecrop is a low growing, evergreen succulent with short flower-bearing spikes. Small white star-shaped flowers tinged with pink on the outer edge of the petals. Perennial. Height 2-10 cm. Flowers Jun-Sep.

Succulents are plants with stems or leaves modified to become thickened and fleshy to retain water in arid climates. This colourful wild flower is now being used in 'green housing' where insulation is provided by plants that are allowed or actively encouraged to grow on roofs.

English Stonecrop (*Sedum anglicum*)
Briweg y Cerrig Family Crassulaceae

The Spotted Rock-rose is Anglesey's county flower and is a locally rare species. The flowers are pale yellow with a dark crimson spot at the base of each petal. It flowers only once during its lifetime and sheds its vivid petals within hours of doing so. Annual. Height 2-15 cm. Flowers Jun-Aug. Near threatened.

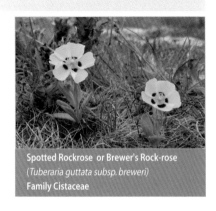

Spotted Rockrose or Brewer's Rock-rose
(*Tuberaria guttata subsp. breweri*)
Family Cistaceae

The Spotted Rock-rose is confined to North Wales, found only on coastal cliff-tops. Most populations are on the west coast of Anglesey between South Stack and Rhoscolyn. Porth Diana in Trearddur Bay became a nature reserve in 1979 primarily to ensure the protection of the Spotted Rock Rose. This small reserve is part of the nationally important coastal heath on the west coast of Holy Island. Characteristic plants here include Bell and Common Heather and in the open patches of grassland, wildflowers such as Spring Squill and English Stonecrop can also be seen.

South Stack Fleawort (*Tephroseris integrifolia subsp. maritima*)
Family Asteraceae

The plant has a rosette of leaves at the base with a single leafy stem bearing a few yellow, daisy-like flowers. It is a subspecies of the Field Fleawort. Biennial or short-lived perennial. Height 5-60cm. Flowers May-Jun. Vulnerable.

This is a schedule 8 plant (protected species) found only on the grassy cliff-tops of South Stack. There are a handful of these plants growing down the steep cliff face near the RSPB Ellin's Tower but are too dangerously situated to view. Most are found a short walk away in an easterly direction. Here *Tephroseris integrifolia subsp. maritima* covers the steep cliffs, including the inaccessible cliff which projects into the sea.

Has heads of numerous small, yellow-green flowers in clusters. Upright fleshy leaves. Perennial. Height to 45 cm. Flowers Jun-Aug.

Rock Samphire (*Crithmum maritimum*)
Corn Carw'r Mor Family Apiaceae

Leaves may be eaten raw or cooked and have a flavour similar to fennel but with a strong salty taste. The leaves may be added to salads. Rock Samphire is little used in herbal medicine though it is a good diuretic. It has a high vitamin C and mineral content and is thought to relieve flatulence and to act as a digestive remedy. It can also be brewed as a tea.

Golden Samphire has leaves having an aromatic scent and large, yellow, daisy-like flowers on long stems. Perennial. Height 15-80 cm. Flowers Jul-Aug. Nationally scarce.

There are several samphires but all belong to different genera. None are related to each other. Samphires were believed to be herbs of St Peter (Saint Pierre) because they grew by the sea. The name St Pierre became corrupted to samphire. In the past Golden Samphire was pickled in the same way as Rock Samphire but was considered inferior.

Golden Samphire (*Inula crithmoides*)
Cedpwydd Suddlon
Family Asteraceae

A delicate plant with cushions of fleshy, strap-shaped leaves close to the ground. Fine branched flowering stems bearing numerous spikes of attractive bluish-lilac coloured flowers. Perennial. Height 8-30 cm. Flowers Jul-Sep.

Rock Sea-lavender (*Limonium binervosum agg.*) Llemyg y Mor-greigiau Family Plumbaginaceae

Despite the common name, Rock Sea-lavender is not related to the Lavender.

Splayed flowering stems bearing white (sometimes pinkish) flowers. Small flowers at the centre with larger, more irregular, flowers at the periphery. Biennial. Height to 100cm. Flowers Jun-Aug. Nationally scarce.

Sea Carrot (*Daucus carota subsp. gummifer*) Family Apiaceae

Recent evidence suggests that the plant, when prepared as an essential oil, has anti-fungal and anti-inflammatory properties.

COASTAL HABITATS

Sand Dunes

Sand dunes are an example of an eco-logical succession. They develop in a series of stages or seres which successively occupy an area from the initial stage to the climax community. Anglesey contains some of the finest examples of coastal dune eco-

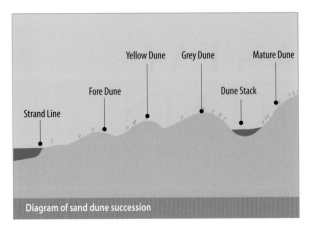

Yellow Dune   Grey Dune   Mature Dune

Fore Dune   Dune Stack

Strand Line

Diagram of sand dune succession

systems in the UK with some recognised as being of international significance. These dunes are well developed on the west coast of the island, particularly around Newborough, Aberffraw and Rhosneigr, where sand is carried inshore by the prevailing south-west winds. On the east coast a small area of dunes occur in Lligwy and Dulas bays.

With increasing distance inland, the number of species and degree of ground cover also increases, demonstrating the time taken for soil development and the resulting increase in availability of moisture, humus and nutrients. Shrubs and woodland are found only on the oldest, most stable dunes further inland. At sites with limited human disturbance this woodland may approach the climax vegetation for sandy soils in an area.

Inland from the strand-line (a mark especially of washed-up seaweed or other debris, showing a previous high water level along a shore) Sea Sandwort and Prickly Saltwort may be observed. Embryo dunes develop and pioneer species such as Marram Grass colonise the dunes. Sea Holly may also be seen. In semi-fixed dunes Red Fescue begins to appear and in the fixed dunes numerous species are present. In the depressions between the dunes (dune slacks) water availability is not an issue and conditions are very different to those in the dunes themselves and a distinctive wetland flora may be found.

Dune building

Sand dunes can develop wherever there is a supply of dry sand grains mobilised by the wind. In coastal locations they depend on a sufficiently wide beach at low tide, allowing dry sand to be picked up and blown inland. A dune grows as sand grains come to rest around obstacles on the beach such as seaweed or driftwood, behind dune ridges or around foreshore plants such as Sea Rocket. The main sand-binding and dune building pioneer species is Marram Grass.

Seaweed torn off rocks and carried in by storm waves rots and releases sufficient nutrients to allow pioneer species to colonise the dune. The establishment of Marram Grass helps to shelter, stabilise and add humus to the soil, enabling other, less hardy plants to colonise the dunes. These plants are adapted to the low soil water content and have leaf adaptations which reduce transpiration. As these plants die they gradually add humus (the organic component of soil, formed by the decomposition of leaves and other plant material by soil microorganisms) to the soil, increasing its water-holding capacity. Embryo dunes may disappear as soon as they form but some are successfully colonised by plants and the sand stabilised. Conditions here are very extreme with a high pH, rapid drainage, no humus, high wind speed and much sea spray. The surface sand is therefore often dry and there is a lack of shade from the sun.

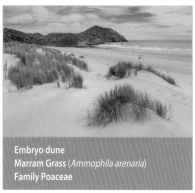

Embryo dune
Marram Grass (*Ammophila arenaria*)
Family Poaceae

Marram Grass is an example of a xerophyte which colonises sand dunes

Rainwater rapidly percolates through the large sand particles and Marram Grass possesses deep roots to reach the water table and is adapted to reduce water loss in dry, windy conditions. It belongs to the Grass family and forms stiff, hardy clumps of erect stems. The leaves are thick and coated in a white waxy cuticle. It grows from a network of thick rhizomes (modified underground stems) which give it a sturdy anchor in its sand substrate and allow it to spread outward. One clump can produce 100 new shoots annually. The rhizomes tolerate submersion in sea water and can break off and float in the currents to establish the grass at new sites. Perennial. Height 1.2m. Flowers Jul-Aug.

Human trampling of dune systems can cause dune erosion. Marram Grass is planted to repair eroding sand dunes as it can grow up through accumulating sand. In Trearddur Bay there is a good example of the success of this approach where the area above the promenade has been fenced off and Marram Grass planted at regular intervals.

It is recorded that in the 16th century Marram Grass was used by the people of Newborough and Aberffraw to weave mats, ropes and baskets. A fibre obtained from the stems is used for making paper.

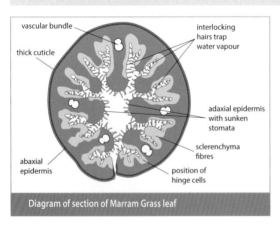

Diagram of section of Marram Grass leaf

vascular bundle

thick cuticle

interlocking hairs trap water vapour

adaxial epidermis with sunken stomata

sclerenchyma fibres

abaxial epidermis

position of hinge cells

Marram Grass shows the following modifications:

The leaves are curled over on themselves. Large thin-walled cells at the base of the grooves shrink when they lose water from excessive transpiration causing the leaf to roll with its upper surface inwards. This reduces the leaf area exposed to air and thus reduces transpiration. It also creates a humid or moist microclimate within the leaf. Instead of being flush with the leaf surface the stomata are sunken and occur in depressions or grooves on the inner surface. This means that humid air is trapped in these depressions outside the stomata. The rate of diffusion through the stomata is therefore significantly reduced. There are no stomata on the outer surface which is exposed to the atmosphere. In the depressions there are stiff, interlocking hairs designed to trap water vapour on the inner part of the leaf and reduce the entry of atmospheric air. The leaves possess a thick, waxy layer over the outer leaf surface. This waterproof layer reduces water loss.

Fore dunes

The first plants to colonise the fore dunes are Lyme Grass, Sea Couch Grass and Marram Grass. As they grow up through the sand they help trap more sand and so the dunes increase in height. Other pioneer plants include Sea Rocket, Saltwort and Sea Holly.

Sea Rocket (*Cakile maritima*) Hegydd Arfor Family Brassicaceae

A member of the Cabbage family the plant has pale, lilac flowers and shiny, fleshy leaves. Annual. Height 15-50cms. Flowers Jun-Sep.

Leaves, stems, flower buds and immature seed pods may be eaten raw and have a strong, peppery flavour similar to horseradish or wasabi, so make a tasty salad addition. The roots, resembling radishes, are also edible. The plant is rich in Vitamin C and can be cooked but becomes very bitter.

Prickly Saltwort (*Salsola kali subsp.kali*)
Helys Ysbigog Family Amaranthaceae

It is a highly-branched, dark-green and somewhat sprawling plant with fleshy, short, linear and succulent leaves tipped by sharp spines. Annual. Height 20-60cm. Flowers Jul-Sep. Vulnerable.

It is found in abundance in the Gobi Desert, where many other plants cannot grow due to the high concentrations of salt in the soil. As a low-water-use plant germinating quickly on minimally disturbed soils and relatively free of diseases and parasites it yields around three tonnes per hectare of plant material. Because of its suitability and high yield the plant has been suggested for growth as a fuel source in such arid areas. This plant is weed-like and, having a high tolerance to salt, is ideal for growing in the areas with the least amount of plant life. The Saltwort is adapted to the desert through a taproot system which helps it gather moisture from the soil while the deeper roots stabilize the plant. It is very invasive and when branches become detached can form tumbleweed.

The juice of the fresh plant is an excellent diuretic. Salsolin, one of the constituents of the plant, has been used to regulate blood pressure. An excellent food with a crunchy tender texture. Young leaves and stems may be eaten raw or cooked and can be used as a spinach substitute or added in small quantities to salads. The ashes of the burnt plant were at one time used for making glass and soap and large quantities of the ashes were imported into Britain for this purpose but nowadays a chemical process using salt is employed. The ashes can also be used as a cleaner for fabrics.

Found on mobile dunes. This plant belongs to the carrot family but because of its prickly nature is very different in appearance from its relatives. The plant is spiny with blue-green holly-like leaves and pale veins. The flowers are metallic-blue. A waxy covering helps the plant to retain moisture in the wind-swept and often inhospitable places where it grows.

The young shoots are normally blanched by excluding light from the growing plant and are then used as an asparagus substitute. It is slightly sweet and smells of

Sea Holly (*Eryngium maritimum*)
Celynen arfor (not confirmed)
Family Apiaceae

carrots. The boiled or roasted roots are said to resemble parsnips or chestnuts in flavour. Sea Holly roots were collected on a large scale in the 17th and 18th centuries in England and were made into restorative lozenges. The plant is still used in modern herbalism where it is valued especially for its diuretic properties.

The plant has a basal leaf rosette, often tinged red and one or more slender, leafless stems with solitary, yellow flower heads. Annual. Height 10-20 cm. Flowers late May-Sep. Vulnerable.

Sometimes called a "false dandelion" because the flowers are similar to those of

Smooth Cat's-ear (*Hypochaeris glabra*)
Melynydd Moel   Family Asteraceae

dandelions. The leaves of Cat's-ear may be eaten raw and are usually added to fresh garden salads. However, they may also be steamed or boiled and used as soup or stew ingredients. The flowers, roots and stems may all be consumed. The root can also be used as a coffee substitute, being peeled, grated and roasted just like coffee beans.

Blow out

This is a term used to describe the type of erosion that can occur in a dune system. If one of the pioneer plants, such as Marram Grass, has not established

in an area, wind can blow the dry sand away to such an extent that wet sand is reached close to the water table. At this point dune slacks may develop. Further inland the sand is re-deposited, often around Marram Grass, and a new dune is formed.

Dune system showing blowout

Dune slack

These are found in between the more mature dunes where the water table reaches the surface causing seasonal or even permanent water-logging and surface water. Plants which are well adapted to these damp sheltered hollows

include rushes, sedges, Cotton Grass and Creeping Willow. Unlike almost all other habitats within the dune system, water availability is not an issue for plants in a dune slack. Consequently, slacks develop a distinctive wetland flora. In a dune system this alternation of wet and dry habitats makes sand dunes very rich areas for wildlife.

Dune Slack

The sand at Newborough is particularly rich in fragmented shells producing a soil with a high calcium content, known as a calcareous soil.

Grey dunes

Dunes with a high humus (organic component of soil, formed by the decomposition of leaves and other plant material by soil microorganisms) content are called 'grey dunes' as opposed to the young dunes which are sometimes called 'yellow dunes'. They are much more stable and may be completely covered with vegetation. Marram Grass becomes far less common and appears in isolated patches. Red Fescue, Sand Sedge and Sea Spurge begin to dominate. Small shrubs such as Bramble, Gorse and Buckthorn appear for the first time.

Sea Spurge (*Euphorbia paralias*) Llaethlys y Mor Family Euphorbiaceae

The plant has straight stems with fleshy, grey-green leaves at the tip of which are small, green complex 'flowers'. Perennial. Height 20-40 cm. Flowers Jun-Sep.

When damaged the leaves bleed an acrid white sap that can irritate the skin. Poachers used the poisonous sap extracted from stems of spurges to kill fish.

Mature dunes

The most mature dunes are found several hundred metres from the shore. If left undisturbed they develop a soil which can support shrubs and trees, such as Hawthorn, Ash and Birch.

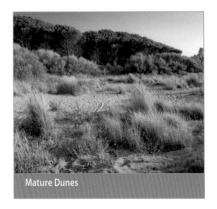

Mature Dunes

Leaching occurs on the dunes, washing humus into the slacks, with the result that the slacks may be much more developed than the exposed tops of the dunes. Leaching also removes calcium carbonate from the upper dunes leading to gradual acidification reflected in a change in the flora of these areas. Eventually this may enable Heather to grow and lead to the establishment of dune heath.

Conservation

In many parts of the UK dune systems have suffered erosion as a result of recreational activity. The destruction of dune systems may result in inland flooding and measures have been taken to protect and stabilise them. A principle management objective has involved the prevention of sand movement and the introduction of structures which defend the land from the sea. Anglesey is fortunate in having several dune systems, particularly Newborough Warren and Aberffraw, which are well maintained and protected. Dune woodland is now a rare habitat in Wales. Fast growing conifers flourish in sandy soils, e.g. in Newborough Forest the planting of conifer plantations on dunes has been extensive.

Dune flora

When visiting a dune system in late spring to early summer, at first glance the dunes may appear uninteresting as Marram Grass is so dominant. However, closer inspection reveals that there are, in fact, a variety of flowering plants to be seen. On the sand hills the yellow, blue or bi-coloured Dune Pansy are found in abundance. Other species include Forget-me-not, Common Storksbill, Sea Spurges (*Euphorbia paralias* and *E. portlandica*), Hound's Tongue, Viper's Bugloss and Common Ragwort.

The small flowers are yellow or pale blue and have five petals, the top two overlapping slightly. There are two smaller wing petals and a single large lower petal with radial reddish-brown honey guides. The leaves are toothed, oval with a heart shaped base. Annual. Height to 30cm. Flowers Apr-Sep.

Dune Pansy (*Viola tricolour subsp. curtisii*)
Trilliw Family Violaceae

These tiny flowers all point south on stable sand dunes. They flower twice a year, in the spring and often again in the autumn. The leaves of wild pansies provide food for Fritillary Butterfly caterpillars.

The tiny green, yellow or purple-tinged drooping flowers are carried on narrow stems above the foliage. Perennial. Height 25-120cm. Flowers Jun-Aug.

An infusion of the leaves, or a decoction of the root, is used in the treatment of fevers.

Lesser Meadow-rue (*Thalictrum minus*)
Arianllys Bach Family Ranunculaceae

Has bright green strap-shaped leaves. The tiny lilac flowers occur in clusters. Annual. Height 3-15cm. Flowers Apr- Jun.

Either from appearing during the lambing season or because it is a favourite food of lambs, the plant is also known as Lamb's Lettuce. The young leaves may be eaten raw and have a mild, nutty flavour suitable for addition to salads.

Common Cornsalad (*Valerianella locusta*)
Llysiau'r Oen Family Valerianaceae

Found in dune slacks Brookweed has spoon-shaped, pale green leaves in the form of a basal rosette and small, white, bell-shaped flowers. Perennial. Height to 45cm. Flowers Jun-Aug.

Brookweed (*Samolus valerandi*) Claerlys Family Primulaceae

S. valerandi may be eaten in salads. Medicinally it has been used as an astringent, a laxative and against scurvy as it has a high vitamin C content. The plant was also often used to heal wounds, rashes and ringworm.

This prostrate plant has fleshy, round leaves and large, attractive, distinctive pink funnel-shaped flowers with five white stripes. Perennial. Flowers Jun-Aug.

Sea Bindweed (*Calystegia soldanella*) Cynghafog Arfor Family Convolvulaceae

The plant is also known as 'The Prince's Flower' after 'Bonnie' Prince Charlie reputedly sowed the seed of the plant after he landed on the Island of Eriskay, Scotland in 1745 to lead the Jacobite rising. The young shoots may be cooked as a vegetable or pickled and used as a Samphire substitute.

A low growing plant having sticky leaves divided into three oval leaflets. It has hairy stems and clusters of small, pink, pea-like flowers. Perennial. Height 10-60cm. Flowers Jun-Sep.

Common Restharrow (*Ononis repens*)
Tagaradr Family Fabaceae

The root may be eaten raw as a liquorice substitute. Soaked in cold water it makes a refreshing cold drink. The young shoots were at one time much used as a vegetable, being boiled, pickled or eaten in salads. It was used widely in Russian herbal medicine.

Oval heads of pale pink flowers covered in soft hairs giving it the downy appearance of the paw of a rabbit or hare, hence the common name. Annual. Height 5-20cm. Flowers Jun-Sep.

Hare's-foot Clover (*Trifolium arvense*)
Meillionen Gedenog Family Fabaceae

The plant has been found to be useful in the treatment of diarrhoea.

Large bright blue, tubular-shaped flowers with white and grey vertical streaks. Has linear leaves. Perennial. Height 10-40cm. Flowers Mid Jul-Sept. Nationally scarce.

Marsh Gentian was used to reduce fever, to counteract poisoning, insect bites and the plague. The plant is particularly important to the Alcon Blue butterfly (*Phengaris alcon*) which lays its

Marsh Gentian (*Gentiana pneumonanthe*)
Family Gentianaceae

eggs on the leaves. A blue dye is obtained from the flowers. The plant is known to be toxic to livestock.

A slender, short, softly hairy plant with lance-shaped leaves in a rosette at the base. Un-stalked, oblong leaves on the stem. Small, bright blue flowers. Annual. Height 15-40cm. Flowers Apr-Jun.

Most stories and myths involving the common name for this plant originated in Germany and the surrounding countries but an English name was in use by the beginning of the 14th century.

Early Forget-me-not (*Myosotis ramosissima*) Ysgorpionllys Cynnar Family Boraginaceae

One myth involves two lovers walking alongside the Danube River where they come across bright blue blossoms. The man retrieved the flowers for his lady but in the process he was swept away by the waters. As he floated downstream he begged her not to forget him.

The plant has fine, low-growing stems bearing small white flowers with five petals. Annual or biennial. Height 5-25cm. Flowers May-Sep.

Seldom used in modern herbalism, the plant was frequently used as a gentle laxative and also for the treatment of muscular rheumatism, liver complaints, jaundice and catarrhal problems.

Fairy Flax (*Linum catharticum*) Llin y Tylwyth Teg Family Linaceae

Low-growing plant with finely-cut leaves and small, pink flowers. Fruits have a distinctive 'beak'. Annual. Flowers Apr-Sep.

Common Storksbill (*Erodium cicutarium*) **Pig y Crëyr Cegidaidd** Family Geraniaceae

Cranesbills and Storksbills are so-called as their seed pods resemble cranes' and storks' bills respectively. Storksbills generally have smaller flowers than their close relatives, Cranesbills.

The plant is also called Pin clover or Pin grass because of its long, thin seed capsules. The seeds have helix-shaped bristly hairs attached to them which aid dispersal as they adhere to the coats of browsing animals and to birds' feathers. The hair also has a corkscrew action which buries the seed in the ground. The hairs are also interesting as they twist or uncurl depending on the humidity in the atmosphere, making them one of nature's barometers.

The young, tender leaves and stems may be eaten raw and added to salads as they have a similar taste to parsley. The root and leaves are the main parts used in traditional medicine and breast-feeding mothers eat these to increase their milk flow. Externally the decoction of the root is used as an antidote to insect bites and to soothe the associated pain. It is also useful for skin infections. In the past an infusion of the plant was given as a remedy for typhoid fever.

The plant is said to control bleeding and is used in Mexico to reduce bleeding after child-birth and to prevent infection. It has astringent and antioxidant properties. In Peru it is used by traditional healers to regulate blood pressure. In the well-known Bach Flower Remedies the Cranesbill is used to relieve obsessive anxiety or worrying.

The plant consists of a cluster of leaves with yellowish bracts at the tip. The oval stem leaves are usually red, as is the stem. The unusual cup-like flower heads lack petals and sepals. Biennial or short-lived perennial. Height 5-30cm. Flowers Apr-Sep.

Members of the Euphorbia family typically produce a white, milky sap called latex that is relatively irritating to humans. However, the sap has some degree of antifungal and antibacterial activity and acts as an excellent wound sealant should the plant be damaged.

Portland Spurge (*Euphorbia portlandica*) Llaethlys Portland Family Euphorbiaceae

A short, creeping plant with square stem and bright green oval leaves, found in opposite pairs. The violet flowers are hooded and two lipped, arranged into a slightly oblong dense head. Perennial. Height to 20cm. Flowers Jun-Sep.

The young leaves and stems can be eaten raw in salads. The aerial parts of the plant can be powdered and brewed in a cold infusion to make a beverage.

Selfheal (*Prunella vulgaris*) Craith Unnos Family Lamiaceae

The plant has greyish-green downy leaves with drooping maroon-red flowers. Biennial. Height 30-60cm. Flowers May-Jul. Near threatened.

Hound's Tongue has a long history of use as a medicinal herb though it is rarely used in modern herbalism. The leaves contain allantoin, a highly effective agent that speeds up the body's healing process. The

Hound's Tongue (*Cynoglossum officinale*)
Tafod y Ci Family Boranginaceae

plant has been used internally in the treatment of coughs and diarrhoea. In modern medicine it is used mainly externally as a poultice on haemorrhoids, wounds, minor injuries, bites and ulcers.

Hound's Tongue contains alkaloids that are especially toxic to cattle and horses. The plant has a disagreeable odour and taste so is seldom eaten by animals but they may inadvertently eat the dried plant in hay. Sheep are more resistant than other livestock to the pyrrolizidine alkaloids.

The leaves at the base are arranged in an upright rosette with bright blue, funnel-shaped flowers. Biennial. Height to 1 metre. Flowers Jun-Sep.

Viper's Bugloss was said to be a cure for various poisons, in particular the venomous bite of a viper.

Echium is derived from the Latin 'echis', a viper.

Viper's-bugloss (*Echium vulgare*)
Tafod y Bwch Family Boraginaceae

Common Cat's-ear (*Hypochaeris radicata*)
Melynydd Family Asteraceae

The long stems bear solitary large, yellow flower heads with numerous florets. The stem arises from a basal rosette of leaves. Perennial. Height 20-40 cm. Flowers Jun-Sep.

Common Cat's-ear is an aromatic plant which has traditionally been used for a wide variety of culinary purposes. The leaves can be steamed and cooked in the same way as any other leafy vegetable and give flavour and texture to dishes such as stir-fries. The raw leaves can also be added to salads as can the petals which are also used to make wine. Cat's-ear is rich in nutrients and antioxidants – hence its popularity in recipes around the world – and therefore has also long been used for medicinal purposes. Uses include acting as a diuretic for kidney problems and for treating urinary infections and gallstones.

Common Ragwort (*Senecio jacobaea*)
Creulys Iago Family Asteraceae

Found in dense clusters of bright, yellow flowers on long stalks. Perennial. Height 30-150cm. Flowers mid Jun-Oct.

The plant is the food source of the black-and yellow-barred caterpillars of the Cinnabar Moth that totally strip the plant of its leaves. Ragwort is poisonous to livestock, particularly horses, damaging the liver when eaten. The toxic effect builds up over time causing irreparable damage.

Slack flora

In contrast to the fast-drying sand dunes, dune slacks are ponds in winter and marshes for most of the summer. Because the conditions are different in the wet hollows between the dunes, a rich flora of different species to those growing on the dunes may be found. Here, the Creeping Willow is dominant and there is an abundance of orchids, particularly Marsh Orchids of several kinds, Marsh and Dune Helleborines and the curious two-leaved Twayblade. Orchids are one of the largest families of flowering plants with as many as 26,000 worldwide. All orchids have three sepals and three petals with a sophisticated structure to ensure cross-pollination.

Leaves hairless on upper surface but hairy on lower surface. Possess separate male and female flowers. The male catkins are white but become yellow when the buds open to expose the anthers. Female catkins are greenish. Height to 1.5m. Flowers Apr-May.

Male catkins

Creeping Willow (*Salix repens*) Corhelygen Family Salicaceae

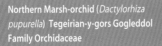

In the past Willow shoots were used in basket-work. More recently they are being utilised as a biofuel.

Flowers are distinctive with spikes of numerous small, deep magenta flowers on long stalks. Perennial. Height 10-30cm. Flowers Jun-Jul.

Northern Marsh-orchid (*Dactylorhiza pupurella*) Tegeirian-y-gors Gogleddol Family Orchidaceae

There are several subspecies. Grow profusely in the dune slacks of Newborough Warren where the flowers are deep red in colour. Perennial. Height 20-40cm. Flowers late May-Jun.

In mid-summer the Early Marsh-orchid exploits the general lack of flowers in damp habitats and bumblebees are attracted by their colourful, though nectar-less flowers. The flower is also visited by flies and beetles.

Early Marsh-orchid (*Dactylorhiza incarnata*) Tegeirian y Gors Family Orchidaceae

Marsh Helleborine (*Epipactis palustris*) Caldrist y Gors Family Orchidaceae

Tall erect stem bearing distinctive clusters of triangular shaped flowers with a frilly white lip. Perennial. Height 20-45cm. Flowers late Jun-early Aug.

During the winter dune slacks become partially submerged after prolonged rainfall. This creates ideal conditions for Marsh Helleborines which carpet the ground each year in early July when the surface rainwater has eventually dried up. Considered by many to be the most beautiful of our wild species because of its exotic looking flowers.

Dune Helleborine has pale yellow-green leaves which protrude from either side of the stem at an acute angle. The flowers are pale yellow-green with faintly tinged pink petals. Perennial. Height 20-50cm. Flowers late Jun-mid Aug. Rare.

Dune Helleborines growing in Newborough Forest are exceptionally tall whereas plants in the nearby exposed sand dunes are much shorter. In late June and early July Dune Helleborine grows among Willow in the dunes.

Dune Helleborine (*Epipactis dunensis*)
Caldrist y Twyni Family Orchidaceae

'Twa blades' or two blades is the origin of the common name of this wild orchid and refers to the single pair of opposite leaves at the base of the flowering stem. The long, slender flower spike is distinctive with numerous small, green flowers. Perennial. Height 20-60-cm. Flowers late Apr-Jun.

This was one of the first orchids to be recognised in Britain. It is now very widespread throughout the country and grows in many habitats. It is often overlooked given its largely green colouration. In ancient times the flowers were incorporated in ointments to heal wounds.

Common Twayblade (*Neottia ovata*)
Ceineirian Family Orchidaceae

One to three slender stems are produced from a rosette of greenish-yellow leaves. At the apex of each is a violet-blue flower. Perennial. Height 5-18 cm. Flowers May-Jul.

Common Butterwort has the alternative common names of Bog Violet and Marsh Violet. Folklore belief said that when cows' udders were rubbed with Butterwort leaves the cows were protected from evil spirits resulting in especially enriched milk and butter. Butterwort is able to thrive on poor, permanently wet, acidic soil. The plant is insectivorous and survives by feeding on insects which become trapped when they land on the sticky leaves. In attempting to escape the insect stimulates the leaf to curl around it and digestive enzymes are released.

Common Butterwort (*Pinguicula vulgaris*) Toddyn Cyffredin Family Lentibulariaceae

Other plants found on Anglesey dune locations

Newborough Warren is an extensive sand dune system and includes the most southerly part of Anglesey at Abermenai Point. The warren is made up of active and fixed dunes and provides an important habitat for many rare plants. The area forms part of a National Nature Reserve (NNR) which includes Malltraeth Sands, the Cob Pool, Cefni Saltmarsh, Abermenai Point, Llanddwyn Island, Llanddwyn Bay and Penrhos Bay. Newborough Forest was first planted in 1947 to protect Newborough from becoming engulfed in sand.

In addition to the Northern Marsh-orchid which is plentiful in Newborough, other orchid species present include Pyramidal Orchid and Common Spotted-orchid (*Dactylorhiza fuchsii*). The Western (or Broad-leaved) Marsh-orchid (*Dactylorhiza majalis* var. *cambrensis*) flowers in May but is difficult to find. Other species particular to that area include Grass of Parnassus, Yellow Bird's-nest, Round-leaved Wintergreen and a minute annual grass, Sand Bent (*Mibora minima*).

There are stunning displays of this beautiful flower in the dune slacks of Newborough.
Heart shaped basal leaves bear long stalks at the apex of which is a single white flower with five petals. Perennial. Height 10-30 cm. Flowers Jul-Aug.

Grass of Parnassus (*Parnassia palustris*)
Brial y Gors Family Celastraceae

This is not a grass at all! The name refers to Mount Parnassus in Greece where it is said that at one time the plant formed a grass-like carpet on the mountainside. The plant has several medicinal uses and may be harvested in the summer or autumn and dried for later use. A decoction is occasionally used as a mouthwash. The dried and powdered plant can be sprinkled onto wounds to aid the healing process. Water distilled from the plant is an excellent astringent eye lotion.

Found in the dune slacks. Round, evergreen leaves and long-stalked stems with clusters of pale flowers towards the tip. Perennial. Height 10-30cm. Flowers Jun-Sep. Nationally scarce.

The name 'Wintergreen' was a term given to plants which are now referred to as 'evergreen'. The oil obtained from the leaves is used as flavouring in chewing-gum and toothpaste. It is also a strong-smelling ingredient in many therapeutic liniments rubbed on various parts of the body to help ease muscle and joint pain.

Round-leaved Wintergreen (*Pyrola rotundifolia subsp. maritima*) Coed-wyrdd Crynddall Family Ericaceae

Yellow Bird's-nest (*Hypopitys monotropa*)
Cyd-dwf Family Cornaceae

A strange-looking herbaceous plant which lacks leaves. Yellow shoots with a waxy appearance appear above ground. The downward drooping tubular flowers become erect in fruit. Perennial. Height 8-20 cm. Flowers Jun-Aug. Endangered.

Found in dune slacks with Creeping Willow. Also known as Dutchman's Pipe, False Beech-drops and Pinesap. The plant is pale yellow as it lacks chlorophyll and cannot photosynthesise. It is frequently found growing under pines and this gave rise to the name, Pinesap. The genus name *Hypopitys* comes from the Greek '*hypos*' meaning under and '*pitys*' pine. *Monotropa* means once-turned. Recent research shows it to be epi-parasitic on the fungus of the genus *Tricholoma* that lives at the base of pine trees, using the fungus to extract nutrients and water from its host, the pine tree. Yellow Bird's-nest is able to live for years completely under the ground.

Autumn Gentian (*Gentianella amarella*) Crwynllys Chwerw
Family Gentianaceae

The plant has dark green spear-shaped leaves with bell-shaped purple flowers which only open fully in sunlight. Biennial. Height 3-30cm. Flowers Jul-Oct.

Gentian root is used in the treatment of digestive disorders. It is especially useful in states of exhaustion from chronic disease and in all cases of debility, weakness of the digestive system and lack of appetite.

The flower heads of Devil's-bit Scabious sit on long stalks and are blue or violet-blue. Perennial. Height to 1m. Flowers late Jun-Sep.

The plant was formerly known by the Latin name 'Scabiosa succisa' which refers to the herb's use in the past to treat scabies. 'Succisa' means 'bitten off' or 'cut off' and refers to the shape of the root. The common name Devil's-bit Scabious derives from folklore where it is suggested that the devil bit off a

Devil's-bit Scabious (*Succisa pratensis*)
Clafrllys Gwreidd-don Family Dipsacaceae

piece of the root so it would lose its power to heal. The herb was probably used first as an herbal medicine in Europe in the Middle Ages. It was not only used to treat scabies but also for external wounds, poisonous insect bites, ringworm, thrush, intestinal worms, epilepsy, gonorrhoea and even the plague. The plant contains tannins, saponins, glycosides, starch, caffeic acid and mineral salts. The thick, glossy leaves were once used to dye wool green.

Seaside Centaury (*Centaurium littorale*)
Canri Goch Arfor Family Gentianaceae

The plant has a basal rosette of narrow leaves and tips resembling spoons. From these arise straight stems, singly or in twos or threes with vivid pink, funnel-shaped flowers, stalk-less at the apex. Biennial. Height to 25cm. Flowers Jul-Aug. Nationally scarce.

Ragged Robin (*Silene flos-cuculi*)
Carpiog y Gors Family Caryophyllaceae

The stalked leaves at the base are oblong to strap-shaped. Pale to bright purplish pink flowers appear in loose clusters. Perennial. Height to 75cm. Flowers May-Jul.

The species name *flos-cuculi* means 'flower of the cuckoo' and was probably chosen because the first flowers of Ragged Robin appear just as the first cuckoos are heard in May.

The roots of these wild flowers are a source of saponin, a soap substitute than can be used for washing clothes or as a shampoo etc. Saponin is toxic although not readily absorbed by the human body; it affects some creatures more than others and has in the past been used by hunters or poachers to stun fish in ponds and streams.

The Aberffraw dune system is one of the most extensive examples of mobile dune habitat in the UK. It is situated to the east of the village of Aberffraw, across the Afon Ffraw. The dunes, along with Traeth Mawr Beach and Llyn Coron have been designated as a SSSI. The area also forms part of the Abermenai to Aberffraw Dunes Special Area of Conservation (SAC). The site supports one of the largest Lyme-grass communities in Wales, and the mobile dunes at the southern end of the reserve contain an abundance of Sea Holly. The types of plants that can be found in the areas of fixed dunes include Red Fescue, Lady's Bedstraw, Marram Grass and early Sand-grass. A number of the slacks contain an abundance of Creeping Willow along with a diverse range of flowering plants including Marsh Orchids, Pyramidal Orchids and Helleborines.

Wild Thyme (*Thymus polytrichus*) Gruwlys Gwyllt Mwaf Family Lamiaceae

Wild Thyme occurs in dense mats topped with whorls of pink-purple flowers. Perennial. Height to 10cm. Flowers May-Sep.

It is used in cooking where its fragrant scent and taste provide a flavoursome seasoning particularly for poultry and pork. As it contains thymol, medicinal uses for wild thyme and its oils include a digestive tonic and mild antiseptic. In manufacturing, red thyme oil is used in perfumes and also in soaps and cosmetics. In the past sprigs were placed under the pillow to aid sleep and posies of wild thyme were used to ward off infectious diseases. It has also been used to make a type of tea and to scent clothes and linen.

Lady's Bedstraw (*Galium verum*) Briwydden Felen
Family Rubiaceae

The plant has small, narrow leaves that appear in whorls on the stems and bear numerous tiny, bright-yellow four-petalled flowers. Perennial. Height 15-60cm. Flowers Jun-Aug.

The dried plant has the scent of newly mown hay. It was formerly scattered (strewn) over the floors of dwellings. Strewing herbs usually have fragrant or astringent odours and many also serve as insecticides or disinfectants.

The name 'bedstraw' refers to its use as a stuffing for mattresses as it was reputed to repel fleas.

The chopped up flowering tops of the plant have the property of curdling milk as the first stage in cheese making, hence the common name 'Cheese Rennet'. Rennet was used in the making of Cheshire cheese, its rich colour probably originally derived from this plant although the colouring is now obtained from annatto. It has been used in Gloucestershire for the same purpose, either alone or with the juice of the stinging-nettle.

The leaves, stems and flowering tops also have medicinal uses, most importantly for treating kidney stones, gravel and urinary disorders in general, and as a tonic and diuretic. It is also used as a poultice to treat skin infections, external ulcers and wounds.

This erect orchid bears bright-pinkish flowers which are first pyramid shaped but become cylindrical. Perennial. Height 20-60cm. Flowers early Jun-mid Jul.

The scientific name *Anacamptis* comes from a Greek word meaning 'bend forward', while the Latin name *pyramidalis* refers to the pyramidal shape of the inflorescence. The dried and ground tuber, which should be harvested as the plant dies down after flowering and setting seed, gives a fine white powder called salep. This very nutritious sweet and starch-like substance is used in drinks, cereals and for making bread. It is also incorporated in diets for children and convalescents, being boiled with water, flavoured and prepared in the same way as arrowroot.

Pyramidal Orchid (*Anacamptis pyramidalis*)
Tegeirian Bera Family Orchidaceae

The Bee Orchid has distinctive pinkish petals with the appearance of a bumblebee attached. Perennial. Height 10-45cm. Flowers Jun-early Jul.

Other species of the genus *Ophrys*, such as the Early Spider and Fly Orchids, have an elaborate pollinating mechanism. Newly emerged male bees are attracted by 'false pheromones' emitted by the orchids. They attempt to copulate with the flower and in

Bee Orchid (*Ophrys apifera*)
Tegeirian y Gwenyn Family Orchidaceae

so doing pick up pollen which is subsequently transferred to the next flower visited. However, the Bee Orchid is the exception as it is self-pollinated.

Autumn Lady's-tresses (*Spiranthes spiralis*) Ceineirian Troellog Family Orchidaceae

A slender plant with small white scented flowers that spiral around the stem from near the base to the apex. The lower flowers open first and are often fading before the uppermost flowers have opened. The plant is unusual in that large clumps may appear in an area but then seem to disappear only to reappear some years later. Perennial. Height 3-20 cm. Flowers Aug-Sep. Near threatened.

The tuberous root has been used as an aphrodisiac. A tincture of the root has been used as a homeopathic remedy and in the treatment of skin conditions, painful breasts, kidney pain and eye complaints.

Creeping stems with pairs of heart shaped leaves at regular intervals. Small, pink lightly-veined, bell-shaped flowers grow singly on short upright stalks. Perennial. Height to 20cm. Flowers May-Sep.

The genus name *Anagallis*, comes from the Greek and means 'to delight again' - a reference to the reopening of the flowers each day when the sun shines. The specific epithet *tenella* means 'delicate or tender'. Extremely fragile, the plant is likely to break as soon as touched.

Bog Pimpernel (*Anagallis tenella*)
Gwlydd y Gors Family Primulaceae

COASTAL HABITATS

Shingle

SHINGLE

Shingle is a particularly unstable habitat as the pebbles are moved about by the action of the waves and plants cannot survive long without being crushed. Three areas of shingle may be found on Anglesey - at Red Wharf Bay, Traeth Dulas and Cemlyn. The latter will be dealt with in greater detail but a mention is made of the vegetation at Red Wharf Bay.

Red Wharf Bay is a large bay located on the north-east coast of Anglesey where a very small, highly sandy area of calcareous shingle stretches out into the north western section of the bay. The vegetation at Red Wharf Bay may be divided into three main categories. The first is a very open, sandy pioneer community found on the steep exposed foreshore and is characterised by the presence of Curled Dock, Sea Mayweed and Sea Sandwort. The second community is grassland with Clover found in varying proportions. There is another area of grassland where areas of Thrift are found.

Curled Dock has smooth leaves from a large basal rosette, with distinctive waved or curled edges. The flowers and seeds occur in clusters on branched stems with the largest cluster being found at the tip. Perennial. Height 50-120cm. Flowers May-Oct.

Curled Dock (*Rumex crispus subsp.littoreus*)
Tafol Crych Family Polygonaceae

Most plants of the Rumex genus, docks and sorrels, are edible, rich in protein, vitamins A and C, bioflavonoids, iron and magnesium. However, they also contain varying levels of tannins and oxalates, the latter giving the leaves of many members of this genus an acid-lemon flavour. Safe in small quantities, the leaves should not be eaten in large amounts since the oxalic acid can lock-up other nutrients in the food, especially calcium, thus causing mineral deficiencies. The oxalic acid content will be reduced if the plant is boiled changing its cooking water several times. Curled Dock or Yellow Dock

(*Rumex crispus*) has an ancient history as a powerful purifying, cleansing herb, used to help heal a wide range of skin conditions and other chronic illnesses.

Sea Mayweed has large daisy-like flowers with yellow centres and white outer petals. The feathery leaves are finely divided. Perennial. Height to 60cm. Flowers May-Sep.

When crushed, the leaves yield a sweet smell similar to that of its relative Chamomile, though less pungent. It has antioxidant properties and is used to reduce inflammation and redness caused by daily stresses.

Sea Mayweed (*Tripleurospermum maritimum*) Amranwen Arfor Family Asteraceae

Sea Sandwort is a low-growing mat-forming plant with yellowish-green, fleshy leaves and with single white-petalled flowers. The plant has creeping runners that make it well adapted to growing in the unstable pebbles. Perennial. Height 5-15cm. Flowers May-Jul.

Sea Sandwort (*Honckenya peploides*) Tywodlys Arfor Family Caryophyllaceae

This plant was named after German botanist Gerhard August Honckeny (1724–1805). The young shoots contain high levels of vitamins A and C and have a delicious flavour eaten raw or cooked. The leaves can also be fermented and used like sauerkraut.

The best example of a shingle bar is found at Cemlyn Bay on the north coast. The storm beach and shingle bar at Cemlyn extend for almost one third of a mile in length. It is regarded by the Anglesey County Council as the 'jewel in the crown' of its AONB. It is valued for both its scenic qualities and its unique range of wildlife. The land has been leased by the North Wales Wildlife Trust since 1971. It includes a large lagoon separated from the sea by a spectacular, naturally created shingle ridge which is known as Esgair Cemlyn, dividing the open sea from a saline coastal lagoon which is considered to be the best example of its type in Wales. The site was designated a SSSI in 1958.

Shingle beach at Cemlyn

The bay and surrounding land forms part of the Cemlyn Estate which is owned by the National Trust. The lagoon was created in the 1930s by the wealthy eccentric Captain Vivian Hewitt. He lived at Bryn Aber, which is situated on the western side of the bay. His interest in birds led him to construct the first dam and weir at Cemlyn, replacing tidal salt marsh with a large and permanent lagoon which he intended as a refuge for birds. Over the following decades various changes have taken place. Storms have caused the sea to break over the ridge and swamp the lagoon. Other changes are man-made with the reconstruction of the weir in the 1970s. The water level and salinity of the lagoon is now monitored to maintain the ideal habitat for terns and other wildlife.

Although a particularly unstable habitat above the strand-line at Cemlyn the stones are large and are not subject to movement. Nevertheless, this area is subject to significant sea spray and consequently many of these plants are adapted to withstand high salinity. In addition to the more common plants found on shingle beaches, such as Sea Beet, Thrift, Sea Campion, Yellow Horned Poppy and Crisped Dock there is also an area of Sea Kale. Around the edges of the lagoon, salt marsh plant communities are present with species such as Sea Aster, Sea Purslane, Danish Scurvy Grass and Salt Marsh Oraches. Set slightly back from the coastal edge of the reserve are boggy areas where wild orchids such as Early Marsh-orchids and Marsh Helleborines can be found flowering from late May through to mid-July.

Sea Beet (*Beta vulgaris subsp. maritima*)
Betysen Arfor Family Amaranthaceae

This plant has large lower leaves and long stems with leafy spikes bearing tiny, green flowers. Perennial. Height to 1m. Flowers Jun-Sep.

It is a close relative of some cultivated beets, such as Sugarbeet, Swiss Chard and Beetroot. The whole plant is edible from the spikes of green flowers to the reddish stems and its beetroot-like roots. It is also known by other common names, Sea Spinach, Wild Beet, Wild Spinach. It is a halophyte, tolerating relatively high levels of sodium in its environment.

In ancient times the leaves and roots of the Sea Beet were used in the treatment of several diseases, particularly tumours. Sea Beet juice has also been used as a treatment for ulcers. In recent years it has been cultivated as a crop. It has an earthy taste and robust texture and can be used in place of spinach but its saltiness also makes it a great addition to a fish dish.

The Yellow Horned-poppy is a straggly coastal plant with golden yellow flowers which appear in June and are followed by the 'horns', curling seedpods that can be up to 30cm long. When damaged the plant exudes a poisonous yellow sap. Biennial to perennial. Height to 90cm. Flowers Jun-Sep.

Yellow Horned-poppy (*Glaucium flavum*) Pabi Corniog Melyn Family Papaveraceae

Glaucium, the generic name, comes from the Latin *'glaucus'* or the Greek *'glaukos'* and is a reference to the glaucous (waxy-blue-green or greyish) colour of the leaves. The specific epithet *flava* means yellow. In the past oil produced from the seeds of Yellow Horned-poppy was used to make soap. It was also burned in lamps. Yellow Horned-poppy seed oil contains glaucine, an alkaloid that can be used in cough medicines. The plant was at one time applied to bruises - hence it being known in south-east England as 'Bruiseroot' or 'Squatmore' (a squat being another term for bruise).

Sea Kale (*Crambe maritima*) Ysgedd Arfor Family Brassicaceae

The plant grows in clumps of large curled cabbage-like leaves with dense white flower heads. Perennial. Height 30-50cm. Flowers late May-Jul.

Once a common seaside plant found on stable shingle and sand above high water mark, Sea Kale has declined due to the commercialisation of many beaches. Popular in Victorian times the blanched young shoots were eaten as a vegetable. Recently the plant has regained popularity with chefs as commercial growers nurture their first crops. The flavoursome shoots taste similar to asparagus and celery.

Red Bartsia has slender erect stems with spikes of small reddish-pink flowers. Annual. Height to 30cm. Flowers Jun-Sep.

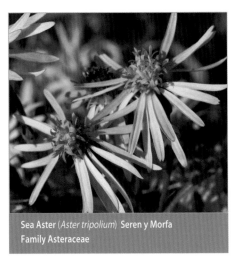

Red Bartsia (*Odontites vernus*) Gorudd Family Orobanchaceae

Sea Aster (*Aster tripolium*) Seren y Morfa Family Asteraceae

Sea Aster is a tall plant with fleshy leaves and flower heads of pale blue-purple but occasionally white. Biennial. Height typically 50cm. Flowers Jul-Oct.

A halophyte which colonises areas frequently flooded by tides. The leaves have a distinctive sweet taste and may be cooked or pickled.

A small evergreen shrub having pale, greyish-green, fleshy, strap-shaped leaves which become narrower up the stem. The inconspicuous flowers are unisexual, with neither the tiny male or female flowers having petals. Perennial. Height to 80cm. Flowers Jul-Sep.

Sea Purslane (*Atriplex portulacoides*)
Family Amaranthaceae

Sea Purslane is a sea vegetable. The edible, matt green leaves may be cooked. They have a plump, fleshy, crunchy texture with a sea-salt taste and are packed with vitamins and minerals. In the Caribbean it is made into a paste to treat puncture wounds from venomous fish.

The plant has tiny, greenish flowers borne on long, branched spikes which are leafy towards the base and on straight, ridged stems. The leaves are narrow and strap-like with the lower leaves short-stalked and the upper leaves un-stalked. Annual. Height 50-100cm. Flowers Jul-Oct.

Grass-leaved Orache (*Atriplex littoralis*)
Llygwyn Arfor   Family Amaranthaceae

COASTAL HABITATS

Mudflats &
Salt Marshes

Mud flats are found where the shore is protected from waves and the gentle movement of salt water inland brings fine sediments which settle out as mud. At high tide the mud flat is covered with water but at low tide the intertidal mud is exposed as a mud flat leaving water only in permanent channels. If mud has built up above the high tide line it may be covered with a habitat called a salt marsh. Salt marsh plants (called halophytes) are capable of living with their roots in salt water and help to stabilise the mud and hold it in place just above the high tide line.

Salt marsh at Red Wharf Bay

The growth of the halophytes helps to consolidate the layers of sediment that have gradually accumulated. Erosion is reduced so the salt marsh increases in height over time. Salt marsh soil is composed of deep mud and peat and because the soil is frequently submerged by the tides and contains a lot of decomposing plant material, oxygen levels in the peat can be extremely low. Halophytes, especially pioneer species such as Sea Meadow Grass and Glasswort (*Salicornia* sp.), are adapted to live in these conditions. These habitats may be found in different degrees of development in many places on the island, except on the western and northern shores of Holy Island and the north coast of Anglesey.

Salt marsh succession

Succession is the serial development of different vegetation types at one place in time. Primary succession occurs when bare mud at the seashore is colonised by plants. Gradual accumulation of additional layers of sediment and plant material increases the height of the marsh and reduces tidal influence. Over time new organisms replace existing ones and species diversity increases until a stable state is reached.

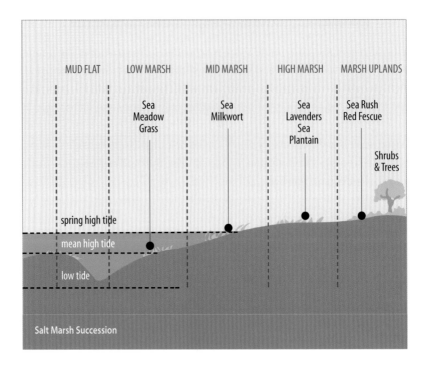

Salt Marsh Succession

Reduced water-logging of the soil and increased freshwater percolation reduces the salinity of the soil. As a result plant communities change with shore height and frequency of submergence, eventually reaching effectively terrestrial but coastal plant communities. On the lower parts of the marsh, dense hummocks of Sea Meadow Grass appear in pioneer communities. Towards the mid marsh increasing numbers of other species appear; Sea Milkwort, Common Sea Lavender, Sea Plantain and Thrift. In the high marsh where the soil salinity has decreased Sea Meadow Grass becomes out-competed by Red Fescue (*Festuca rubra*) and Sea Rush (*Juncus maritimus*) communities. Without intervention, such as grazing, the salt marsh communities would essentially move further offshore with the gradual accumulation of sediment.

Some of the species of flowering plants commonly found on salt marshes are:

Glassworts are highly specialised and appear to be merely jointed, succulent stems lacking leaves but on closer examination they do possess pairs of small, triangular leaves. The flowers are inconspicuous and are pollinated by wind. Also called Marsh Samphire.
Annual. Height 10 to 45cm. Flowers Aug-Sep.

Sea Meadow Grass (*Puccinellia maritima*) in the tidal zone

Common Glasswort (*Salicornia europaea*)
Llyrlys Cyffredin Family Amaranthaceae

In his writings William Shakespeare made reference to Samphire growing on the White Cliffs of Dover. Samphire Hoe is an area of land reclaimed during the construction of the Channel Tunnel. It was developed into a country park and named after the Rock Samphire that was once collected from the Dover cliffs.

The young stems are edible and have a salty taste. They can be pickled or eaten as a garnish. Its bright green stalks resemble asparagus spears, hence one of its alternative names – Sea Asparagus. Once described as the poor man's Asparagus it is now much in demand as a culinary speciality. It is also known as Glasswort as the ash was once used as a source of soda ash (mainly sodium carbonate) for glassmaking. Also used in soap production.

The leaves are short, roundish, flat on the upper surface and taper to a blunt tip. Has green flowers (sometimes purple or red) and lacks petals. Found in small bunches in the axils of leaves. Annual. Height to 30cm. Flowers Jul-Sep.

Annual Sea Blite (*Suaeda maritima*) **Helys Unflwydd** Family Amaranthaceae

The leaves absorb a great deal of salt and eventually turn red when oversaturated. If the salt is extracted from the leaves and left to dry it turns black. This explains Seablite's Latin name *Suaeda*, which comes from the Arabic and means 'black salt'. The ashes of the plant provide a soda that is used in making glass and soap. The young leaves may be eaten raw or cooked and have a pleasant salty flavour.

The leaves form a dense tuft with straight stems bearing small flowers varying from green to purple. Perennial. Height to 60cm. Flowers May-Sep.

Other common names are Coriander Grass and Wild Coriander because it is edible and has a similar taste to coriander. The very young flower shoots appear with flower buds which may be eaten. Other edible parts of the plant are the pale white/green ends of the leaves, found at the base which smell distinctly of coriander when crushed. Dark green leaves should be avoided as they are poisonous.

Sea Arrow Grass (*Triglochin maritima*) **Saethbennig Arfor** Family Juncaginaceae

Low growing with fleshy stems and leaves. Small, pink flowers. Perennial. Height 10-30cm. Flowers May-Aug.

Sea Milkwort (*Glaux maritima*)
Family Primulaceae

The young shoots may be eaten raw or pickled and the roots may be consumed after prolonged cooking. It may be used as a sedative, some native North American Indians ate the boiled roots to induce sleep.

Low growing with small, cylindrical fleshy leaves and whitish-pink flowers.
Perennial. Height to 30cm. Flowers May-Sep.

Greater Sea Spurrey (*Spergularia media*)
Troellys Mawr Family Caryophyllaceae

The root has been used as an emetic (an agent used to induce vomiting).

Has narrow, fleshy leaves growing in tufts. Long flowering spikes with numerous yellow stamens. Perennial. Height to 30cm. Flowers Jun-Sep.

Sea Plantain (*Plantago maritima*)
Llwynhidydd Arfor
Family Plantaginaceae

The young leaves may be eaten raw or cooked and have a delicious flavour, often added to a mixed salad. The seed can be ground into a powder and used as a flour extender.

Fleshy leaves and clusters of flowers which are usually white but occasionally mauve. Biennial/perennial. Height 5-30 cm. Flowers Apr-Aug.

Common Scurvygrass (*Cochlearia officinalis*)
Llwylys Cyffredin Family Brassicaceae

A member of the cabbage family, Scurvygrass is so named because it was used to treat scurvy. This was a common disease of sailors during long sea journeys caused by a lack of vitamin C in their diet.

Waxy, fleshy leaves in a rosette from which grow stalks bearing flowers which range from blue through to lilac and pink. Perennial. Height to 40cm. Flowers Jul-early Oct. Found in Traeth Dulas, where the Afon Goch discharges its waters into an inlet.

Common Sea Lavender (*Limonium vulgare*)
Lafant y Mor Family Plumbaginaceae

Despite its name and colour Common Sea Lavender is not actually a true lavender and does not share its distinctive smell. It is, however, just as popular with butterflies and other insects. It is also one of the best perennials for using as a cut flower, especially for drying. It is recorded as being used in the treatment of abdominal pain. The Elizabethan herbalist John Gerard wrote " the seed beaten into pouder and drunk with Wine, helpeth the Collique".

WETLANDS

Fens & Marshes

Most of the wetlands of the UK have been lost and the remaining ones are very vulnerable to damage. They're often seen as non-productive land so they're filled in or destroyed, without people realising the wider impact for plant, animal and human life. Wetlands are extremely important for the rare plants found there as well as the variety of insects and birds they support. The creation, restoration and sensitive management of wetlands is therefore vital to biodiversity conservation.

In the UK there are three main types of wetlands-fen, bog and marsh. A fen is a wetland which is formed when groundwater seeps into a depression through cracks in a hard clay base which normally does not allow the ingress of water. A major difference between bogs and fens is how they are formed. Almost all of the water in bogs comes from rain and snow whereas fens are fed by groundwater (the water in the soil and rocks underground) and surface water from streams. The presence of fresh water means that fens often have a higher nutrient content and are less acidic and thus support a wider variety of life. Both bogs and fens contain a considerable amount of decaying matter but fens contain less partially decayed plant matter, called peat. Fens can turn into bogs if fresh water stops flowing in, decaying plant matter accumulates and nutrient levels decrease.

A marsh is a wetland often found on the edges of rivers or lakes and is characterised by having mineral soils which are poorly drained and plant life composed mainly of grasses. The defining characteristic of a marsh is that it is constantly flooded with water from a specific source. This source can either be a river, lake, streambed, pond or even ocean. Some marshes are fed by groundwater. However, the majority of them receive water from the sources mentioned above or even from rain. Marshes tend to be rich in mineral deposits. This is because the water movement slows down depositing minerals on the marsh making a marsh rich in plant and animal life. Unlike bogs and fens marshes do not overlay peat. The majority of plants in marshes are grasses, sedges and reeds.

There are three fens on Anglesey. Cors Erddreiniog (the largest), Cors Bodeilio and Cors Goch and are all National Nature Reserves (NNR's). (Cors is Welsh for 'bog'). Normally wetland habitats are on peaty soil over sandstone, granite or other chalk-deficient substrates and are acidic in their composition. The three fens represent a rare type of wetland fed by alkaline water that drains into them from the surrounding porous limestone rocks creating the conditions which support the unusual combination of plants that are found there. Many of these plants, collectively called calcicoles, can exist only in this type of highly alkaline habitat.

Fen at Cors Bodeilo

The following description is confined to flowering plants found in these lime-rich fens.

Cors Goch is one of the jewels in Anglesey's crown of special wildlife loca-tions. The fen has a variety of habitats including extensive reed beds, woodland, heath land and small lakes. The area is home to many specialised plants. It lies near the village of Llanbedrgoch and is a North Wales Wildlife Trust reserve, a SSSI and a NNR. It is also included in the Anglesey Fens Special Area of Conservation (SAC). Cors Goch is a valley mire and a lime-rich fenland and has a layer of peat that exceeds three metres deep in places. It has a somewhat wetter western compartment where Llyn Cadarn is situated. It supports many rare wetland plants - the carnivorous Sundew is a particularly interesting example.

Plants characteristic of fens found in Cors Goch are the locally dominant Saw Sedge (*Cladium mariscus*), Black Bog Rush (*Schoenus nigricans*), Blunt Flowered Rush (*Juncus subnodulosus*) and Bulbous Rush (*Juncus bulbosus*). Also present are rarer sedges including Lesser Tussock-sedge (*Carex diandra*),

Slender Sedge (*Carex lasiocarpa*) and Bog Sedge (*Carex limosa*). Cors Goch has a wonderful collection of wild orchids including Frog Orchid (*Coeloglossum viride*), Lesser Butterfly-orchid (*Platanthera bifolia*), Marsh Fragrant-orchid (*Gymnadenia densiflora*) and several kinds of Marsh Orchids (*Dactylorhiza incarnata, D. purpurella*), Green-winged Orchid (*Anacamptis morio*) and the nationally scarce Narrow-leaved Marsh-orchid. Other plants found growing in a wider range of habitats, are Common Reed (*Phragmites communis*) and Grass of Parnassus (*Parnassia palustris*).

A selection of plants found in these wetland habitats include the following:

A spindly plant with 3-5 narrow, unspotted leaves growing from the base. The upper stem is washed purple and the flower spike is small with large purplish-pink flowers, conspicuously marked. The lip of the flower is three-lobed. Perennial. Height 10-40cm. Flowers Late May-Jul. Nationally scarce.

This orchid is able to survive in Anglesey because of the alkaline flushes which filter down through the limestone rocks in an otherwise acidic area.

Narrow-leaved Marsh-orchid (*Dactylorhiza traunsteinerioides*) Family Orchidaceae

A small deciduous flowering shrub. The flowers are catkins (cylindrical flower cluster with very small or no petals) with male and female catkins on separate plants. Height to 1.5m. Flowers Apr-May.

Male catkins

Bog-myrtle (*Myrica gale*)
Helygen Mair Family Myricaceae

Female catkins

Both the catkins (collected in spring) and the leaves (collected in summer) are high in essential oils. The plant has many uses in herbal medicine. In the past it was used for its astringent, antiseptic, wound healing and diuretic properties. It was also used to dye wool yellow and in candle making. Nowadays it can be found in mosquito repellent and as an ingredient in many perfume products.

Found in shallow water, forms wide mats with leaves just above the water, and pale pink star-shaped flowers. Perennial. Height 15-30 cm (above water). Flowers May-Jun.

The bitter-tasting leaves of the Bogbean have been used in various ways: as a herbal tea to treat irregular menstruation, to strengthen appetite, aid digestion and enhance nutrient absorption. Also as an ingredient to flavour beer.

Bogbean (*Menyanthes trifoliata*)
Ffa'r Gors Family Menyantheaceae

Single, upright branching stem with feathery leaves and deep pink, open-lipped flowers. Annual to biennial. Height to 60cm. Flowers May-Sep.

The plant is also known as Red Rattle and, as the name suggests, produces seeds which rattle in their pods.

Marsh Lousewort (*Pedicularis palustris*) Melog y Waun Family Orobanchaceae

Male flowers

Female flowers

Mountain Everlasting (*Antennaria dioica*)
Edafeddog y Mynydd Family Asteraceae

Has male and female flowers on separate plants. The small female plants bear pinkish flowers in heads on short, straight stems. The tiny male flowers are usually white, bearing soft, downy heads with both plants carrying five to eight in each cluster. The erect stems rise from rosettes of dark green spear-shaped leaves. Perennial. Height 5-20cm. Flowers late May-Jul.

The plant is very rich in mucilage which makes it valuable in the treatment of chest complaints and was at one time used in mixtures for the treatment of bronchitis.

Marsh Arrowgrass is slender and grass-like with numerous, tiny green flowers tinged purple, on a long spike. It gives off a pleasant aromatic smell when bruised. Perennial. Height 15-40cm. Flowers Jun-Aug.

Round-leaved Sundew (*Drosera rotundifolia*)
Gwlithlys Family Droseraceae

Marsh Arrowgrass (*Triglochin palustris*)
Saethbennig y Gors Family Juncaginaceae

Sundew has leaves in small rosettes with a thick coating of red hairs on their upper surface. Small, white flowers appear one at a time on slender stems. Perennial. Height to 5 cm. Flowers Jun-Aug.

The Sundew is carnivorous. Like all plants it is able to make its own food but obtains extra nitrogen and other nutrients by digesting small insects trapped by drops of a sticky liquid found on the hairs of the leaves. Once the insect is stuck fast the leaves fold over it, and enzymes are secreted and start to digest the insect's tissues. After about two days the resulting digested material is then absorbed by the leaf. The plant is named Sundew because the droplets on the leaves were thought to be drops of dew that were retained even in sunny weather. The dried plant has medicinal uses and acts as an expectorant. It can be taken as a tea for various breathing problems including bronchitis, asthma and whooping cough.

Also known as Water Parsley, a member of the carrot family, it has narrow paired leaves and white flowers, sometimes tinged pink. Perennial. Height 30-60cm. Flowers Jun-Sep.

Oenanthe means ' flowers of the vine' as the Greeks thought this plant resembled vine flowers.

Parsley Water-dropwort (*Oenanthe lachenalii*)
Cegiden Dail Persli Family Apiaceae

The plant has leafy stems bearing large, golden-yellow flowers. Perennial. Height 20-60cm. Flowers late Jul-Sep.

As the species name suggests, it was used in the treatment of dysentery. When burnt the dried leaves were thought to emit an odour that would repel fleas. Hence the genus name, *Pulicaria*, from the Latin *pulex*, meaning flea.

Common Fleabane (*Pulicara dysenterica*)
Codowydd Family Asteraceae

The low growing plant has attractive green leaves which are hairy and rounded. Delicate, yellow flowers, which have an odour of resin, are borne on sturdy stalks.
Perennial. Height to 40cm. Flowers Jun-Sep.

Marsh St. John's-wort (*Hypericum elodes*) Eurinllys y Gors Family Hypericaceae

The basal leaves are oval, the stem leaves spear-shaped. Reddish stems bear shiny yellow 5-petalled flowers. Perennial. Height to 50cm. Flowers May-Oct.

All parts of the plant are poisonous when fresh, the toxins are destroyed by heat or by drying. The plant also has a strongly acrid juice that can cause blistering to the skin.
It has been used as a topical application that produces redness of the skin e.g. by causing dilation of the capillaries and an increase in blood circulation. A tincture of the plant is used to cure ulcers.

Lesser Spearwort (*Ranunculus flammula*) Llafnlys Bach Family Ranunculaceae

Very similar to Thistle in appearance with purple-lilac flowers but lacking spines. The common name comes from the saw-like serrations on the edges of the narrow leaves. Perennial. Height 20-70cm. Flowers Jul-Sep.

A yellow dye is obtained from the plant. As a herbal preparation it is thought to heal ruptures and wounds.

Saw-wort (*Serratula tinctoria*)
Dant y Pysgodyn Family Asteraceae

Cors Eirddeiog and Cors Bodeilio are represented by similar species to those growing in Cors Goch. The plant life is unique and very diverse and the plants are specific to the alkaline wet environment and in Cors Bodeilio these include: Black Bog-Rush, Common Reed, Great Fen Sedge, Blunt Flowered Rush and Fen Pondweed. Columbine provides a colourful display in Cors Erddreiniog in early summer. A notable addition is the rare Fly Orchid.

Most of the leaves are found at the base of the stem. The flowers closely resemble small flies. Perennial. Height 15-60 cm. Flowers late May-early Jun. Vulnerable.

Shaped like a 'fly' it secretes sex pheromones which attract the male Digger Wasp. As they attempt to copulate with the flower their heads become covered in pollen. When they

Fly Orchid (*Ophrys insectifera*)
Family Orchidaceae

visit other Fly Orchids they are then pollinated by the contaminated wasps. This activity ceases once the female Digger Wasps emerge two weeks later.

The bonnet-shaped purple or blue flowers are distinctive with five tubular petals and short, hooked spurs. Perennial. Height to 1m. Flowers May-Jun.

The plant is poisonous and in the past posies were given as a message of condemnation to an adulterous wife.

Columbine (*Aqualegia vulgaris*)
Blodau'r Sipsi Family Ranunculaceae

Erect stems bear small clusters of attractive white flowers with a cream centre. Perennial. Height 20-60cm. Flowers Late Jun-Sep.

The specific name *ptarmica* derives from the Greek and means to cause a sneeze. The plant has a pungent scent and dried and powdered leaves from this plant were once used as a 'sneezing powder'. The botanical name *Achillea* stems from the belief that Achilles used flowers of this genus to cure his wounded soldiers

Sneezewort (*Achillea ptarmica*)
Ystrewlys Family Asteraceae

and medicinal properties are claimed for an essential oil that can be extracted from the leaves. During the Middle Ages chewing the acrid roots of Sneezewort was recommended to soothe toothache. Despite its bitter taste, the leaves have also been used in salads. However, it is known to be poisonous to some farm animals, including cattle and horses. Bridesmaids at West Country weddings used to carry posies of Sneezewort in the belief that doing so would ensure a happy life for the bride and groom.

Wild Angelica (*Angelica sylvestris*)
Llys yr Angel Family Apiaceae

A tall plant with hollow, ridged stems and highly-divided light green leaves. The tiny flowers are white or tinged pink and are grouped into domed inflorescences. Perennial. Height 1 to 2m. Flowers Jun-Sep.

The genus name, *Angelica*, means 'angelic' - like an angel. The specific name *sylvestris* often implies 'of the woods' but in this instance it is used in an alternative sense to denote 'growing wild'. Soldier Beetles are among the many insects attracted to the flowers.

The plant has historical significance as a medicinal herb although nowadays the plant's essential oil is primarily used in the manufacture of toothpaste, shampoo and soap. The stems, leaves, seeds and roots of Angelica are all edible. In medieval times it was believed that Angelica had protective powers and people drank Carmelite water (containing Angelica) to ward off spells from witches. In 1665 an outbreak of the Black Death spread throughout London. People were desperate for a cure so the College of Physicians, under the instruction of King Charles II, concocted a tonic which they called 'the King's Majesty's excellent recipe for the plague'. The brew which included treacle, nutmeg and Angelica was slowly stewed and prescribed twice daily to thousands of inhabitants.

It has deeply divided, oblong leaves and thistle-like bright pink flower heads.
Perennial. Height 20-80cm. Flowers Jun-Sep.

In 14th century Britain the plant was known as Matfellon and was eaten with pepper at the start of a meal to stimulate the appetite. Parts of the Knapweed flower are edible and can be added to salads. In Wales the Physicians of Myddfai included Common Knapweed with many other herbs in a potion to counteract the toxins in adder bites. The flower is a source of good quality nectar and is visited by bees, butterflies and beetles. Its seeds also provide food for many birds.

Common Knapweed (*Centaurea nigra*)
Pengaled Family Asteraceae

The genus name *Centaurea* derives from the Centaur Chiron who used flowers of this genus as a poultice to cure a festering wound made by an arrow dipped in Hydra's blood. In the past eligible young women would play a game to foretell their future in love by pulling out the florets of the flower and place the plucked knapweed flower in their blouse. When buds began to bloom it would signify the man of her dreams was near. Medicinally, Knapweed was used for ruptures and wounds, bruises, sores, scabs and sore throats.

A vigorous upright plant with reddish stems, leaves divided into narrow leaflets, and dense domed clusters of tiny, light pink or purple flowers. Perennial. Height to 1.5m. Flowers Jun-Sep.

The flowers are very attractive to all kinds of insects including butterflies such as the Small Tortoiseshell and Red Admiral. The genus *Eupatorium* was named after Mithridates Eupator (134-63 BC), King of Pontus who was a herbalist reputed to be the first to use the Eupatorium genus as a medicine. He was also very knowledgeable about poisons.

Hemp Agrimony (*Eupatorum cannabinum*)
Byddon Chwerw Family Asteraceae

The specific name *cannabinum* means 'hemp-like' and is a reference to the leaves which are similar to those of Hemp or Cannabis plants (for example *Cannabis sativa*) which have been used for making rope. Chemicals found in the herb are thought to stimulate the immune system in a positive way. Hemp Agrimony may be used internally as a herbal tea to increase appetite, aid digestion and to treat rheumatic disorders. The root of the plant can act as both laxative and diuretic. External uses of Hemp Agrimony, in the form of a tincture, include treatment of minor skin infections, bleeding, bruising and wounds.

The leaves are small, coarsely toothed with small, pale lavender or white flowers arranged around a leafy elongated spike. Annual. Height 10-40cm. Flowers May-Sep.

Common Eyebright is a hemi-parasite on the roots of grasses. This means that it is partially parasitic, using specialised roots to penetrate those of its host and obtain some nutrients, the remainder being gained through photosynthesis. As the name implies, the plant has been used as a herbal remedy against weakening vision and a variety of eye conditions including cataracts and conjunctivitis. Other uses include the treatment of respiratory conditions and allergies.

Common Eyebright (*Euphrasia nemorosa*)
Effros Family Orobanchaceae

A delicate plant with white, starry, five-petalled flowers which appear too large for the spindly stems which support them. The small leaves have little tufts in the angle between stem and leaf resembling tiny knots, hence the English name. Perennial. Height 5-15cm. Flowers Jul-Sep.

Knotted Pearlwort (*Sagina nodosa*)
Corwlyddyn Clymog
Family Caryophyllaceae

Knotted Pearlwort has a unique way of reproducing. Besides producing seeds, it also makes bundles of leaves which break off in the autumn. These bundles are carried by water or wind to other suitable areas where they take root. In this way the plant avoids the risky stage of germination.

Pale Dog Violet *(Viola lactea)* Fioled Welw
Family Violaceae

Long, narrow leaves with cream to pale lilac flowers borne on short stems. Perennial. Height to 20cms. Flowers May-Jun. Vulnerable.

This plant is included as a species "of principal importance for the purpose of conserving bio-diversity".

Malltraeth Marsh (Cors Ddyga)

Along the coast from Newborough is an estuary formed by the Afon Cefni, which flows across the island from a point north of Llangefni. Much of the river flows through this low-lying valley, forming the Malltraeth Marsh. The area is recognised as a SSSI and has a range of reed beds, marshes, wet grassland and pools. Ditches occur throughout this area and contain an interesting collection of plants but are difficult to access.

Reed Canary-grass (*Phalaris arundinacea*) Gwyran Family Poaceae is a perennial grass that dominates the area and grows to 1.7m tall. It can quickly become established in wetlands, ditches, and other sites with moist soil. Flowers May-Jul. It can exclude all other vegetation and is extremely difficult to eradicate once established.

Water-plantain (*Alisma plantago-aquatica*) Dŵr-lyriad Family Alismataceae is a perennial usually found in shallow water or exposed mud on the edge of slow-flowing water. It is 20-100cm. in height. Flowers Jun-Aug. Flowers are small, usually white with three petals, occasionally tinged purple.

Branched Bur-reed (*Sparganium erectum*) Cleddlys Family Typhaceae is a perennial found along the edge of slow-flowing water. It is 50-150cm in height. Flowers Jun-Jul. The pale lilac flowers are borne on a many branching inflorescence.

Horned Pondweed (*Zanichellia palustris*) Cornwlyddyn Family Potamegetonaceae is a submerged aquatic plant with inconspicuous flowers and a string-like appearance. Its seeds bear a distinctive horned shape, hence the common name. A perennial with long, tendril-like leaves and roots.

Mare's-tail (*Hippuris vulgaris*) Rhawn y Gaseg Family Hippuridaceae is a perennial found in water margins. It has trailing underwater stems with occasional erect shoots with whorls of leaves and small flowers at the base of the upper leaves. Flowers Jun-Jul.

Autumnal Water-starwort (*Callitriche hermaphroditica*) Brigwlyyd Cynhaeaf Family Callitrichaceae is annual to perennial. The plant is small with submerged leaves and minute flowers lacking petals. Flowers Apr-Oct.

Spiked Water-milfoil (*Myriophyllum spicatum*) Myrdd-ddail Tywysennaidd Family Haloragaceae is a perennial aquatic plant living submerged in slow-flowing areas of water. Its attractive, feathery leaves are held just below the water surface. It bears tiny, dull red flowers in spikes above the water surface, in Jun-Jul.

Blunt-leaved Pondweed (*Potamogeton obtusifolius*) Dyfrllys Gwelltog Family Potamogetonaceae is a perennial and is found submerged in a range of standing water habitats. The plant lacks floating leaves and has minimal flowers on short stalked spikes. Flowers Jun-Sep.

Valley Wetlands

Valley Wetlands RSPB Reserve is situated beside RAF Valley in Anglesey. The site includes two SSSIs, designated for the important open water and aquatic plant communities. With more than 20hectares of reed, it holds one of the most important reed beds in Wales which, together with the surrounding marshes, are home to a rich variety of wetland plants including the nationally scarce Eight-stamened Waterwort (*Elatine hydropiper*), Flowering Rush (*Butomus umbellatus*) and Hop Sedge (*Carex lupulina*). Wild orchids include the beautiful dark-purple Northern Marsh-orchid (*Dactylorhiza purpurella*) and Early Marsh-orchid (*Dactylorhiza incarnata*). In the early summer there are groups of Yellow Iris among the reeds at the edge of the lake.

Yellow Iris (*Iris pseudacorus*) Iris Felen Family Iridaceae

A tall marginal plant forming dense groups of branched stems and large, bright yellow flowers with delicate dark spots and veins on the sepals. Its leaves are elongated and sword-shaped. Perennial. Height up to 1.5m. Flowers May-Jul.

The plant was believed to avert evil and was hung in bunches outside the doors of houses in Ireland on the Feast of Corpus Christi. Medicinally it was used for its astringency to stem blood flow. Also the roasted seeds were used to make a coffee flavoured drink.

Amphibious Bistort (*Persicaria amphibia*) Canwraidd y Dŵr Family Polygonaceae

Long-stalked floating leaves and small pink flowers borne on a spike. The leaves are hairless and have a heart shaped base. Perennial. Height 30-70cm. Flowers Jul-Sep.

Native Americans employed this plant in various ways. The flower heads were used as bait when trout fishing, and when hunting the smoke from the leaves was thought to attract deer. Medicinally, a poultice of freshly gathered roots was used to soothe mouth ulcers, and an infusion of the dried roots was given as a remedy for chest colds. The Welsh physicians of Myddfai used it in remedies against fever.

WETLANDS

Ponds Lakes & Rivers

PONDS, LAKES AND RIVERS

Aquatics are plants that almost always grow in water. Some float on the surface with free roots whilst most are rooted to the bed of the substrate of the pond, lake or river in which they grow. Plants living in an aquatic environment require special adaptations in order to survive submerged in water or on the water's surface. They live in an oxygen-challenging environment. Hydrophytes are aquatic plants that are especially suited for living in such environments. In order to survive hydrophytes have the following adaptations.

- As water is a supportive medium they have little or no supporting tissue.
- Surrounded by water there is little need for transport tissue.
- The leaves have little or no cuticle because there is no need to prevent water loss.
- Stomata are found only on the upper surface of the leaves because the lower surface of floating leaves is in water.
- Stems and leaves have large air spaces, constructed of cells, forming a reservoir of oxygen and carbon dioxide. These spaces allow diffusion of oxygen from the aerial portions of the plant into the roots. Thus the roots do not have to depend on getting oxygen from the soil. These gases also provide buoyancy to the plant.

Apart from the rich fens of the limestone valleys, aquatic habitats include small lakes, rivers, stagnant ditches and marshes. Anglesey has around 20 lakes all located in the western half of the island. The main rivers of Anglesey are Alaw, Braint, Cadnant, Bran and Cefni.

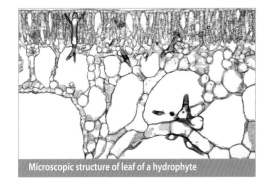
Microscopic structure of leaf of a hydrophyte

Plants found commonly in most aquatic habitats on Anglesey include the following:

The heart shaped leaves are a glossy, dark green. The flower lacks petals, it is the sepals that are a bright yellow. Perennial. Height to 60cm. Flowers May-Aug.

Marsh-marigold (*Caltha palustris*)
Gold y Gors Family Ranunculaceae

The Latin name *Caltha* is derived from the Greek *calathos* (a cup or goblet) from the shape of its flowers. The specific name is derived from the Latin *palus* (a marsh) in reference to its place of growth. The English name Marigold refers to its use in church festivals in the Middle Ages as one of the flowers devoted to the Virgin Mary. It was also used on May Day festivals being strewn before cottage doors and also made into garlands.

All parts of the plant can irritate or blister the skin or mucous membranes and so should be used with caution. However, the leaves are edible and harvested in the spring as the plant is coming into flower and are eaten like spinach after cooking in two or more changes of water. It has been used to remove warts and is also used in the treatment of anaemia. A poultice of the boiled and mashed roots can be applied to sores. A tea made from the leaves is diuretic and laxative.

Found in still or slow-flowing water, the large, shiny, dark-green leaves grow close together on the surface of the water. The large, fragrant white flowers, with conspicuous yellow stamens, are held above the water and open only in sunshine. Perennial. Flowers Jun-Sep.

White Water-lily (*Nymphaea alba*)
Lili-ddŵr Wen Family Nymphaceae

The rhizome (a modified horizontal underground stem that sends out roots and shoots) is antiseptic as well as astringent. An extract of the plant material is effective in curing dysentery or diarrhoea caused by irritable bowel syndrome. Water-lily can also be used to treat kidney pain, congestion and can be gargled to help soothe a sore throat.

It has large 'lily pad' leaves, up to 40cm across, and grows in water up to 3 metres deep with the familiar leaves floating on the surface. The yellow flowers are smaller than those of *N.alba*. Perennial. Flowers Jun-Sep.

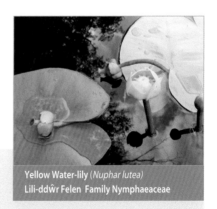

Yellow Water-lily (*Nuphar lutea*)
Lili-ddŵr Felen Family Nymphaeaceae

N. lutea smells like dregs of wine, hence the common name 'Brandy Bottle' among others. Some attribute the name to the large flagon-shaped flowers.

The whorls of close set lilac flowers form a rounded head at the top of the stem. Has a sweet, peppermint scent. Perennial. Height 15-60cm. Flowers Jul-Oct.

Water Mint has both culinary and medicinal uses. Water Mint tea is considered to be effective in settling upset stomachs and as a mild sedative. In the Middle Ages Water Mint plants were strewn on the floors of grand houses to release a pleasant odour when walked upon.

Water Mint (*Mentha aquatica*)
Mintys y Dŵr Family Lamiaceae

Mentha, the generic name, comes from Greek mythology in which the naiad Minthe (variably spelt also as Menthe, Mintha or Mentha) was transformed into a sweet-smelling mint plant by Persephone, daughter of Zeus and queen of the underworld.

The deep magenta flowers are unusually shaped. They appear as two five-pointed stars, one smaller and deep purple, set above another, larger and paler. Its leaves are serrated and tinged blue-green on their underside. Perennial. Height 20-50cm. Flowers May-Jul.

Marsh Cinquefoil (*Comarum palustre*)
Pumdalen y Gors Family Rosaceae

The common name 'cinquefoil' derives from the French 'cinq feiulles' and refers to the five grouped leaflets that make up the leaves of most members of the Potentilla genus. The specific name 'palustris' means marshy.

Marsh Cinquefoil is a good source of nectar for bees and flies. A weevil, *Phytobius comari,* which feeds exclusively on the plant is known as the 'Marsh cinquefoil weevil'.

Tannin is obtained from the root and in the past was used to dye leather a reddish-yellow colour. A red dye was also produced from the flowers. The leaves are reputed to make a pleasant tea drink. A number of medicinal uses were found for its astringent roots. An extract may be used in the treatment of dysentery and stomach cramps.

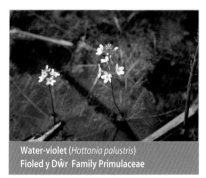

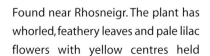
Water-violet (*Hottonia palustris*)
Fioled y Dŵr Family Primulaceae

Found near Rhosneigr. The plant has whorled, feathery leaves and pale lilac flowers with yellow centres held above the water. The long stems are rooted to the bottom of ponds. Perennial. Height up to 80cm. Flowers May-Jun.

Listed as one of the 38 plants used to prepare Bach Flower Remedies. It is also a good oxygenator of garden ponds.

Frog-bit (*Hydrocharis morsus-ranae*)
Alaw Lleiaf Family Hydrocharitaceae

Found in Llyn Llygeirian. The plant has rosettes of small, free-floating heart shaped leaves surrounding a white flower with three petals and yellow centre. Its roots hang down into the water but do not normally reach the bottom. Perennial. Flowers Jul-Aug. Vulnerable.

Eight-stamened Waterwort (*Elatine hydropiper*) Family Elatinaceae

Found in Llyn Coron the plant forms a carpet on the water surface. The very small leaves are ovate-oblong with pale red flowers, a maximum 2 mm in diameter. Annual. Height 2-4 cm. Nationally scarce.

Has a very limited distribution in the British Isles. Anglesey is one of its strongholds.

Greater Spearwort (*Ranunculus lingua*)
Llafnlys Mawr Family Ranunculaceae

Found in Llyn Rhos Ddu, Llyn Dinam, Cors LLanddyfnan, Cors Bodeilio and near Rhosneigr.
The plant has long narrow leaves and large, bright glossy yellow flowers. Perennial. Height 50-120cm.
Flowers May-Sep.

This tall plant has strong, erect stems, with long, poker-like heads of bright purple-red flowers which are extremely attractive to bees and butterflies. Perennial. Height 60-150cm. Flowers Jun-Aug.

A decoction (a method of extraction by boiling) of the plant is impregnated into wood, rope etc to prevent it rotting in water, probably due to the preservative effect of its tannin content. The powdered plant is used cosmetically in face-packs to counteract reddened skin. Medically it is an astringent herb that is mainly employed as a treatment for diarrhoea and dysentery.

Purple Loose-strife (*Lythrum salicaria*) Llys y Milwr
Family Lythraceae

CALCICOLES AND CALCIFUGES

Calcicoles

Plants that thrive on lime-rich soils are called calcicoles. Examples of such soils on Anglesey are to be found where there are carboniferous limestone outcrops. These areas are a narrow strip along the Menai Strait west of Menai Bridge, Puffin Island and around Penmon Point. Also from the north side of Red Wharf Bay along the coast to Lligwy Bay and extending inland in a narrow strip beyond Llangefni and parallel to Malltraeth Marsh on the north side.

In places where shell fragments have accumulated there provides a lime-rich habitat for calcicoles. One such area is found along the eastern side of Red Wharf Bay. On Llanddwyn Island, where Pre-Cambrian rocks such as those found in South Stack normally yield acid soils, banks of blown sand containing shell fragments have created conditions for the growth of lime-loving plants.

The plant displays an inflorescence of up to 50 dark purple flowers arranged in a dense, cone-shaped cluster on a tall spike. The glossy leaves are dark green with dark spots, and form a rosette on the ground. Perennial. Height 10-45cm. Flowers Apr-Jun.

Early-purple Orchid (*Orchis mascula*) Tegeirian Coch Family Orchidaceae

One of the orchids from which the drink salep is produced. This is a starchy drink made from the dried and powdered tuber. It was sold in salep shops in London in the 17th century and later. Salep has a number of medicinal uses particularly for digestive problems including heartburn, flatulence. Salep is also used to treat diarrhoea, particularly in children. Known to be beneficial for treating impotence in men, an extract obtained from the flower has been known to successfully treat erectile dysfunction. Legend has it that witches administered a drink made from the fresh tubers of Salep Orchid to promote true love and a potion brewed with its withered tubers cured lovesickness!

Common Rock-rose (*Helianthemum nummularium*) Cor-rosyn Cyffredin Family Cistaceae

A low, spreading evergreen shrub with tiny, oval leaves and yellow flowers. Perennial. Height 5-50cm. Flowers May-Sep.

Although it produces neither scent nor nectar the Rock-rose is visited by insects gathering pollen.

The flower is commonly used in Bach Flower Remedies. It is taken to alleviate panic, stress, extreme fright or fear, anxiety, and for promoting calmness and relaxation.

Similar to Common Rock-rose but with smaller flowers. Perennial. Height stems to 25cm. Flowers May-Jul. Nationally scarce.

Also used in Bach Flower Remedies to alleviate panic, stress, extreme fright or fear, anxiety, and for promoting calmness and relaxation.

Hoary Rock-rose (*Helianthemum elandicum*)
Family Cistaceae

The plant is low growing, hairy, often prostrate, branching from the base. Has pale green, three-lobed leaves. The flowers are green and lack petals. Annual. Height 2-10cm. Flowers Apr-Oct.

The plant has a history of use in herbalism being commonly employed to rid the body of stones in the kidney or bladder. It continues to be in use to this day for the treatment of kidney stones and water retention.

Parsley-piert (*Aphanes arvensis*)
Troed y Dryw Family Rosaceae

Confused Eyebright (*Euphrasia confusa*)
Effros Gliniog Family Orobanchaceae

Has small, serrated leaves and tiny white to purple flowers. Annual. Height 2-45cm. Flowers May-Sep.

The Euphrasia genus contains approximately 18 species of plants. They are hemi-parasites of low fertility grasslands, particularly dry habitats on calcareous soils. The plants parasitise and draw nutrients from the roots of a wide range of meadow plants including grasses and legumes. The common name refers to the plant's use in treating eye infections.

Wild Majoram (*Origanum vulgare*)
Penrhudd Gwyllt Family Lamiaceae

Erect stem with dark purple buds at the apex that open to show purple, pink or occasionally white bunches of thyme-like flowers. Long, oval leaves usually slightly toothed and sweetly scented. Perennial. Height 30-60cm. Flowers Jul-Sep.

The flowers of Wild Marjoram are particularly attractive to butterflies. It is a relative of Oregano which is an important flavouring herb in Mediterranean cookery and is often used dried rather than fresh. It is a popular ingredient of pizza, pasta sauces and Greek salads as well as a flavoursome addition to chicken, fish and roast vegetables.

Medicinal uses of Oregano include treating respiratory tract disorders, gastrointestinal and urinary tract disorders and menstrual cramps. Applied topically, it may help treat a number of skin conditions such as acne and dandruff. It is strongly sedative and should not be taken in large doses, although mild teas have a soothing effect and aid restful sleep. Oregano is often used in the form of an essential oil that is distilled from the flowering plant and used in aromatherapy products. A few drops of the oil, put on cotton wool and placed in the hollow of an aching tooth is said to relieve the pain. Early herbalists used both Oregano and Wild Majoram for their powerful antiseptic properties.

Has distinctive leaves and a rounded flower head of small green flowers. The uppermost flowers are female, the central flowers bisexual and the lower flowers male. Perennial. Height 15-40cm. Flowers Jun-Sep.

The leaves smell and taste pleasantly of cucumber and were commonly added to salads at one time. Medicinally it was used as a dressing to stem bleeding wounds. The species name *sanguisorba* is Latin for 'sanguis' or 'blood' and is related to *sorbere* meaning to soak up.

Salad Burnet (*Poterium sanguisorba*)
Bwrned Family Rosaceae

Carline Thistle *(Carlina vulgaris)* Ysgallen Siarli   Family Asteraceae

Carline Thistle is an unattractive spiny plant with distinctive brown and golden flower heads which resembles a thistle gone to seed but it is, in fact, in full flower. This is a very common plant on the dunes of Newborough. It remains in bud for some time before the flower actually opens in July to August and by the end of September it has finished flowering. Biennial. Height 10-60cm. Flowers Jul-Oct.

The flower head acts as a natural hygrometer as it is sensitive to the level of moisture in the environment. It closes whenever the humidity rises above a certain point making it useful as a primitive weather forecasting device. A closed flower is taken as an indicator that rain is approaching. Foul smelling when freshly plucked from the ground, the root develops a pleasant aroma when dried. While young and still in the bud stage, the flower heads can be cooked and eaten like globe artichokes. The plant was often referred to as 'hunter's bread'. In the past some cultures attached the floral head to the front of dwellings to bring good luck.

Medicinally the plant is used as a remedy for colds, its root also serving as an effective diuretic. When applied externally it brings relief to various skin conditions such as acne and eczema. During the Middle Ages the soldiers of the Emperor Charlemagne of Germany's army were dying from plague. Folklore has it that an angel gave the ruler this herb to stem the tide of the epidemic. From then on the plant was named in his honour. Subsequently, it has been discovered that Carline Thistle contains the acetylide carlina oxide (*furylbenzylacetylene*), the main compound of the essential oil from the plant. This chemical has a long history of medicinal use in Europe due to its anti-microbial properties. It is thought to be active against two strains of MRSA and a number of other resistant bacteria.

The plant has long-stalked, deeply divided leaves each with five to seven bi-lobed or tri-lobed leaflets with large, solitary flowers. Perennial. Height 10-40. Flowers May-Aug.

Bloody Cranesbill (*Geranium sanguineum*) Pig yr Aran Rhuddgoch Family Geraniaceae

Geranium, the genus name, comes from the Greek noun *geranos* meaning 'crane' and is a reference to the beak-like fruit (seed capsule) which is reminiscent of the long beak of a crane. The specific *sanguineum* comes from the Latin *sanguineus*, meaning 'blood' and is a reference to the colour of the flower stalks and seed capsules which turn bright red.

The oil of the Geranium makes a good astringent and can be diluted with water and used topically to clean the face or be added to a bath. It also has antiseptic properties and is said to help restore the balance of dry or oily skin and hair. The leaves and flowers can be made into a tea.

Herb-paris (*Paris quadrifolia*) Cwlwm Cariad Family Melanthiaceae

The four oval leaves are positioned in opposed pairs at the apex of the otherwise leafless stem. The single flower at the tip is inconspicuous and has a crown of golden-yellow stamens.
Perennial. Height 15-40cm. Flowers Late Apr-Jun.

The common name 'herba paris' was first used in 1544 by Italian botanist Pierandrea Matthioli. Herb Paris also appears in Gerard's Herbal of 1636 as an antidote to highly toxic substances such as arsenic or mercury. Other common names allude to its black berry (devil-in-a-bush) or to its connections with love – the four leaves are paired like lovers and also bear a resemblance to the loops of the true lover's knot. Other sources consider that Herb Paris's generic name *Paris* is a reference to the Trojan prince who, in Ancient Greek mythology, was asked by the god Hermes to give a golden apple to the most beautiful goddess. The plant's four leaves represent Paris and the three competing goddesses, and the berry growing at the top is the apple. In fact the word 'paris' in the name of this plant has nothing to do with the city in France but comes from the Latin word 'par' meaning 'equal' and simply refers to the symmetry of the leaves.

Calcifuges

Plants that cannot tolerate alkaline (basic) soils are called calcifuges. These plants grow only or mainly on acidic soil. They are found typically on cliffs and mountainsides where the soil is free-draining, infertile and acidic and is characterised by open, low-growing woody vegetation such as Heather and Gorse and includes coarse grasses. On Anglesey these thin, acid soils have been derived from Pre-Cambrian rocks and are found on Mynydd Llwydiarth in the south east, on Mynydd Bodafon further towards the north east, around Mynydd Parys and on Holyhead Mountain. Smaller areas of heath also occur in other areas of the island. In the Cors Goch area and at Rhos Lligwy, acid soils derived from the Carboniferous era may be found bearing heath vegetation. Two plants of importance are Marsh Gentian found in abundance in the area of Rhos Lligwy, and the Pale Dog Violet in Cors Goch. In the wetter parts of the heaths there are patches of Bog Asphodel an indicator of mineral-deficient soils.

Bog Asphodel (*Narthecium ossifragum*) Llafn y Bladur   Family Nartheciaceae

The pyramidal flower spikes carry a dense cluster of up to 20 yellow, star-like flowers. Once the flowers have died the fruiting stems turn bright orange. Perennial. Height 10-45 cm. Flowers Jul-Aug.

The plant was used to make yellow dye and also as a substitute for saffron in cooking. The Latin name *ossifragrum* refers to the belief that the legs of sheep that grazed on the plant became brittle and broke easily. There is no evidence to support this and it is more likely that the terrain favoured by Bog Asphodel, which is treacherous and also tends to be low in nutrients, was the real cause of such injuries to animals.

Lousewort (*Pedicularis sylvatica*) Melog y Cŵn Family Orobanchaceae

Low growing with sprawling stems bearing pinkish-purple flowers. The plant (also known as Dwarf Red Rattle) is much shorter and a more spreading plant than its relative Marsh Lousewort. Perennial. Height 10-20cm. Flowers Apr-Jul.

The genus name Pedicularis is from the Latin 'pediculus' meaning louse. The common name, Lousewort, applies to several species and derives from an old belief that when eaten by livestock the plants were responsible for lice infestations. In the past herbalists considered the Red Rattle a wound healing herb and stypic.

Amphibious Bistort (*Persicaria amphibia*)*   105
Annual Sea Blite (*Suaeda maritima*)   84
Autumn Gentian (*Gentianella amarella*)*   64
Autumn Lady's-tresses (*Spiranthes spiralis*)   70
Bee Orchid (*Ophrys apifera*)*   18,69
Bell Heather (*Erica cinerea*)   31
Bloody Cranesbill (*Geranium sanguineum*)   119
Bog Asphodel (*Narthecium ossifragum*)   121
Bogbean (*Menyanthes trifoliata*)*   91
Bog Myrtle (*Myrica gale*)   91
Bog Pimpernel (*Anagallis tenella*)*   71
Brookweed (*Samolus valerandi*)*   52
Carline Thistle (*Carlina vulgaris*)   117
Columbine (*Aqualegia vulgaris*)   97
Common Bird's-foot-trefoil *(Lotus corniculatus)**   36
Common Butterwort (*Pinguicula vulgaris*)*   62
Common Cat's-ear (*Hypochaeris radicata*)   58
Common Cornsalad (*Valerianella locusta*)*   51
Common Eyebright (*Euphrasia nemorosa*)*   101
Common Fleabane (*Pulicaria dysenterica*)*   94
Common Glasswort (*Salicornia europaea*)   83
Common Heather (*Calluna vulgaris*)   31
Common Knapweed (*Centaurea nigra*)*   99
Common Ragwort (*Senecio jacobaea*)   58
Common Restharrow (*Ononis repens*)*   53
Common Rock-rose (*Helianthemum nummularium*)   114
Common Scurvygrass (*Cochlearia officinalis*)   86
Common Sea Lavender (*Limonium vulgare*)   86
Common Storksbill (*Erodium cicutarium*)*   19,55
Common Twayblade (*Neottia ovata*)   61
Confused Eyebright (*Euphrasia confusa*)*   116
Creeping Willow (*Salix repens*)   59
Cross-leaved Heath (*Erica tetralix*)   31

Curled Dock (*Rumex crispus subsp. littoreus*)   73

Danish Scurvygrass (*Cochlearia danica*)[1]   36

Devil's-bit Scabious (*Succisa pratensis*)*   64

Dune Helleborine (*Epipactis dunensis*)[2]   61

Dune Pansy (*Viola tricolour curtisii*)   51

Early Forget-me-not (*Myosotis ramosissima*)*   54

Early Marsh-orchid (*Dactylorhiza incarnata*)*   60

Early Purple Orchid (*Orchis mascula*)*   114

Eight-stamened Waterwort (*Elatine hydropiper*)   112

English Stonecrop (S*edum anglicum*)   37

Fairy Flax (*Linum catharticum*)*   54

Fly Orchid (*Orphrys insectifera*)   96

Frog-bit (*Hydrocharis morsus-ranae*)   112

Golden Samphire (*Inula crithmoides*)   39

Gorse (*Ulex europaeus*)*   33

Grass of Parnassus (*Parnassia palustris*)*   63

Grass-leaved Orache (*Atriplex lottoralis*)   79

Greater Sea Spurrey (*Spergularia media*)   85

Greater Spearwort (*Ranunculus lingua*)   112

Hare's-foot Clover (*Trifolium arvense*)*   53

Hemp Agrimony (*Eupatorum cannabinium*)*   100

Herb-paris (*Paris quadrifolia*)   119

Herb-Robert (*Geranium robertum*)*   19

Hoary Plantain (*Plantago media*)   24

Hoary Rock-rose (*Helianthemum canum*)[3]   115

Hound's Tongue (*Cyanoglossum officinale*)*   57

Kidney Vetch (*Anthyllis vulneraria*)   34

Knotted Pearlwort (*Sagina nodosa*)*   101

Lady's Bedstraw (*Galium verum*)   68

Lesser Meadow-rue (*Thalictrum minus*)*   51

Lesser Spearwort (*Ranunculus flammula*)   95

Lousewort (*Pedicularis sylvatica*)*   122

Marram Grass (*Ammophila arenaria*)   43-45

Marsh Arrowgrass (*Triglochin palustris*)*   91

Marsh Cinquefoil (*Comarum palustre*)*   110

Marsh Foxtail (*Alopecurus geniculatus*) 24
Marsh Gentian (*Gentiana pneumonanthe*) 53
Marsh Helleborine (*Epipactis palustris*) 60
Marsh Lousewort (*Pedicularis palustris*)* 92
Marsh Marigold (*Caltha palustris*) 108
Marsh Samphire (*Salicornia europaea*) see Common Glasswort 84
Marsh St. John's-wort (*Hypericum elodes*)* 95
Meadow Cranesbill (*Geranium pratense*) 19
Mountain Everlasting (*Antennaria dioica*) 92
Northern Marsh-orchid (*Dactylorhiza purpurella*) * 59
Narrow-leaved Marsh-orchid (*Dactylorhiza traunsteinerioides*) 90
Pale Dog Violet (*Viola lactea*) 102
Parsley Water-dropwort (*Oenanthe lachenalii*)* 94
Parsley-piert (*Aphanes arvensis*)* 115
Portland Spurge (*Euphorbia portlandica*)* 56
Prickly Saltwort (*Salsola kali*) 46
Purple Loose-strife (*Lythrum salicaria*)* 113
Pyramidal Orchid (*Anacamptis pyramidalis*)* 69
Ragged Robin (*Silene flos-cuculi*)* 66
Red Bartsia (*Odontites vernus*)* 78
Rock Samphire (*Crithmum maritimum*) 39
Rock Sea-Lavender (*Limonium binervosum*)[4] 40
Rock Sea-spurrey (*Spergularia rupicola*) 35
Round-leaved Sundew (*Drosera rotundifolia*) 91
Round-leaved Wintergreen (*Pyrola rotundifolia subsp. maritima*) 63
Salad Burnet (*Poterium sanguisorba*)* 117
Saw-wort (*Serratula tinctoria*)* 96
Sea Arrow Grass (*Triglochin maritima*) 84
Sea Aster (*Aster tripolium*)* 78
Sea Beet (*Beta vulgaris subsp . maritima*)* 76
Sea Bindweed (*Calystegia soldanella*) 52
Sea Campion (*Silene uniflora*) 35
Sea Carrot (*Daucus carota subsp. gummifer)** 40
Sea Holly (*Eryngium maritimum*) 47
Sea Kale (*Crambe maritima*) 77

Sea Mayweed (*Tripleurospermum maritimum*)*   74
Sea Milkwort (*Glaux maritima*)   85
Sea Plantain (*Plantago maritima*)   85
Sea Purslane (*Atriplex portulacoides*)   79
Sea Rocket (*Cakile maritima*)   45
Sea Sandwort (*Honckenya peploides*)   74
Sea Spurge (*Euphorbia paralias*)   49
Seaside Centaury (*Centaurium littorale*)   66
Selfheal (*Prunella vulgaris*)*   56
Sheep's-bit Scabious (*Jasione montana*)   37
Shining Cranesbill (*Geranium lucidum*)   19
Smooth Cat's-ear (*Hypochaeris glabra*)   47
Sneezewort (*Achillea ptarmica*)*   97
South Stack Fleawort (*Tephroseris integrifolia subsp. maritima*)[5]   38
Spotted Rockrose or Brewer's Rockrose (*Tuberaria guttata subsp. breweri*)   37
Spring Squill (*Scilla verna*)*   34
Thrift (*Armeria maritima*)   33
Viper's-bugloss (*Echium vulgare*)   57
Water Mint (*Mentha aquatica*)*   110
Water Violet (*Hottonia palustris*)   111
Western Gorse (*Ulex gallii*)   33
White Water-lily (*Nymphaea alba*)   109
Wild Angelica (*Angelica sylvestris*)*   98
Wild Majoram (*Origanum vulgare*)   116
Wild Thyme(*Thymus polytrichus*)   67
Yellow Bird's-nest (*Hypopitys monotropa*)   64
Yellow Horned-poppy (*Glaucum flavum*)   77
Yellow Iris (*Iris pseudacorus*)   104
Yellow Water-lily (*Nuphar lutea*)   109

Cover photo:'South Stack Fleawort' by **Karen Woolley**
(https://karenwoolley.blogspot.co.uk)

ACKNOWLEDGEMENTS

Map of Anglesey: Anglesey County Council
www.anglesey.gov.uk/Journals/w/x/m/Anglesey-AONB

'Salt Marsh, Red Wharf Bay' (www.geograph.org.uk/photo/4428540)
© Copyright N Chadwick and licensed for reuse under
creativecommons.org/licenses/by-sa/2.0

'Dune slack in the Raven Meols Hills'
(www.geograph.org.uk/photo/1859373)
© *Copyright* **Gary Rogers** *and licensed for* **reuse** *under this*
Creative Commons Licence.
'Cemlyn Bay" and "Fen at Cors Bodeilo' by Gareth Rowlands

Flowering plant index of photographs

Photographs marked with asterisk * are by **Hugh Knott**
(www.cambriaflora.net)

Photographs without asterisk are from Shutterstock, except:

[1] 'Cochlearia danica (Danish Scurvy-grass) on cliffs near Crozon, France'
(https://commons.wikimedia.org/wiki/File:Cochlearia_danica
_Crozon_060416w.jpg)
By User: Strobilomyces [GFDL (http://www.gnu.org/copyleft/fdl.html)
or CC- BY-SA-3.0 (http://creativecommons.org/licenses/by-sa/3.0/)],
from Wikimedia Commons

[2] 'Inflorescence of Epipactis dunensis on Anglesey sand-dunes'
(https://commons.wikimedia.org/wiki/File:Epipactis_dunensis
_inflorescence.jpg)
By Velella [CC BY-SA 3.0 (https://creativecommons.org/licenses/by-sa/3.0)],
from Wikimedia Commons

3   'Hoary Rock-rose flower' (https://commons.wikimedia.org/wiki/
    File:Hoary_rockrose_flower.jpg)
    By Velela [Public domain], from Wikimedia Commons
4   'Limonium binervosum, Family: Plumbaginaceae, Image No. 3'
    (https://commons.wikimedia.org/wiki/File:Limonium
    _binervosum2.jpg)
    By Kurt Stüber [GFDL (http://www.gnu.org/copyleft/fdl.html) or CC-BY-
    SA-3.0 (http://creativecommons.org/licenses/by-sa/3.0/)],
    via Wikimedia Commons
5   'Sea Kale on Cemlyn' by Andy Rowlands (www.andyrowlands.com)
6   'Tephroseris integrifolia subsp. maritima on South Stack'
    (https://commons.wikimedia.org/wiki/File:Tephroseris
    _integrifolia_subsp.maritima.JPG)
    By Velella [CC BY-SA 4.0 (https://creativecommons.org/licenses/by-
    sa/4.0)], from Wikimedia Commons

Local organisations

For information on wildlife sites and nature reserves on Anglesey contact North Wales Wildlife Trust, Head Office, 'Llys Garth', Garth Road, Bangor, Gwynedd, LL57 2RT Phone: 01248 351541 Email: nwwt@wildlifetrustswales.org Website: www.northwaleswildlifetrust.org.uk

For more information on Anglesey flora and if you are interested in botanical fieldwork and recording on Anglesey, contact the Anglesey Flora Group, c/o Treborth Botanic Garden, Bangor University, Treborth Road, Bangor, Gwynedd, LL57 2RQ Phone: 01248 353398 Email: treborth@bangor.ac.uk

The Botanical Society of Britain & Ireland (BSBI) is the centre for information on botanical matters throughout Britain and Ireland, with online up-to-date maps of the distribution of all species. Website : www.bsbi.org